EMOTIONAL
FREEDOM
TECHNIQUES

SIMPLE WAYS FOR ATTRACTING
WELL-BEING AND ABUNDANCE

Sangeeta Bhagwat

wisdom
tree

Photograph Credits
Model: Arshiya Kunwar
Photographer: Jay (Aperture India, Pune)

First published 2009

ISBN 978-81-8328-150-8

Published by
Wisdom Tree,
4779/23, Ansari Road,
Darya Ganj, New Delhi-110002
Ph.: 23247966/67/68
wisdomtreebooks@gmail.com

Printed in India at Print Perfect

Contents

Tap Your True Potential with Emotional Freedom Techniques (EFT)

Terms of Use

Important note: Gary Craig, the founder of EFT is not a licensed health professional and offers EFT as an ordained minister and as a personal performance coach. Please consult qualified health practitioners regarding your use of EFT.

This EFT oriented book is provided as a good faith effort to expand the use of EFT in the world. It represents the ideas of the author and does not necessarily represent those of Gary Craig or EFT.

The author, Sangeeta S. Bhagwat, has no formal qualifications in medicine and this book is based on personal use and experience with EFT. The book is intended as a reference volume only. The information given here is designed to help you make personal improvements in performance, health and overall well-being. It is not intended as a substitute for any treatment that may have been prescribed by your doctor. If you suspect that you have a medical problem, we urge you seek competent medical help.

While EFT has produced remarkable clinical results, it must still be considered to be in the experimental stage and thus practitioners and the public must take complete responsibility for their use of it. Hence, you are required to take complete responsibility for your own emotional and/or physical well-being both during and after reading this book. You are also required to instruct others whom you help with EFT, or to whom you teach it, to take complete responsibility for their emotional and/or physical well-being. You must agree to hold harmless the author and anyone involved with EFT from any claims made by anyone whom you seek to help with EFT or to whom you teach EFT. Don't use these techniques to try to solve a problem where your common sense would tell you it is not appropriate.

If you do not agree with the foregoing, or cannot comply, you are advised not to read or use this book.

1 | Introduction

"If you have built castles in the air, your work need not be lost: that is where they should be. Now put the foundations under them."

— Henry David Thoreau

Each and every one of us is blessed with unique talents and abilities. Unfortunately, we also tend to have a lot of barriers inhibiting the full expression of our potential.

In the modern world, high stress and competition continually take their toll. The health and self-esteem of every individual is challenged on almost a daily basis. Environment, conditioning, feedback and expectations from our parents, peers, teachers or bosses, significant events in our lives, the list of contributing factors goes on. Each one of us is weighed down by depression, anger, grief, fear or anxiety to varying degrees, at some point in life. Some of us are able to shrug these off and carry on with optimism and enthusiasm. However, there are many of us who remain pinned down by these negative emotions and beliefs, which weigh us down like a ton of bricks. They inhibit our thoughts, actions and expressions in subtle and obvious ways. You may be aware of some of these limitations, and others may remain in the subconscious. While it may be a fear of failure that prevents you from trying, it could be a fear of success that stops your friend.

Repeated disappointments or failures lead to further uncertainty, erosion of self-esteem and pessimism. The pattern continues through different areas of your life. Over a period of time, this accumulated baggage may trigger cravings or addictions. Suppressed or neglected, they may continually cause a cascade of physiological changes, contributing to stress and stress-induced diseases. Frequently, if not always, physical discomfort or disease may have an emotional contributor associated with it and hence treating the disease alone may not provide desired results. One can end up facing performance, emotional and physical problems, all at one time!

What if help was at hand, to rid your self of every such limiting emotion, thought or belief that you have ever had? What if you found a way to enhance every positive trait that you possess? What if you were able to have assistance in healing your emotional and physical issues, so as to arrive at a state of perfect health and well-being? You may have just found your answers with this book.

Emotional Freedom Techniques can help you unblock your true potential.

2 | How to Use This Book

*"Believe nothing, no matter where you read
it, or who said it, no matter if I have said it,
unless it agrees with your own reason and
your own common sense."*

— Buddha

This book is intended as an introduction of EFT to first time users and those recently acquainted with the subject.

It is deliberately designed to resemble a website, with each chapter being analogous to a web page.

Please ensure that you have read the 'Terms of Use' first. From here, you can directly proceed to 'Getting Started'. Once you have worked satisfactorily with 'Getting Started', you may want to familiarise yourself with 'The Full Basic Recipe'. For any reason, if you are dissatisfied with your results, please see 'When You are Not Seeing Results'.

Titles of subsequent sections are self-explanatory and you should have no difficulty in locating information on your topic of interest. Thus, you are provided with the freedom to jump straight into your area of interest. Reading the entire book in the order provided would be helpful, but is not essential.

Remember to use your common sense and have reasonable expectations of this powerful technique. Sometimes, experiencing quick and impressive results can lead to unrealistic expectations. EFT is a complementary tool to your thinking, philosophy and actions. It is not a substitute for any of these.

If you wish to improve yourself, whether it is your personality, your health, your relationships, your bank balance or your lifestyle you need to behave and do things which are in alignment with those intentions! EFT can help you do all this, as also dissolve any conscious or subconscious limiting thoughts, beliefs or emotions that you may have. However, contrary to a lot of popular material these days, I do not claim that this technique is a quick-fix solution to all problems or a means to easily obtain all your wants and desires.

Personal improvement, whether moral, spiritual, physical, financial or in any other area, is a constant and ongoing process. If you can accept this, then welcome to a highly useful and effective tool that will provide you assistance at every step of your way.

3 Frequently Asked Questions

*"Look and you will find it; what is unsought
will go undetected."*

— Sophocles

3.1: What is energy healing?

Energy healing refers to different modalities of healing which
address disruptions, congestions or imbalance in the subtle
energies of the body. Energy healing is not a new concept
and most Eastern schools of medicine are based on such
premises. Various descriptions and attributes are defined
under different techniques; reiki, qui gong, acupressure,
acupuncture, pranic healing, *pranayam*, etc. Different
schools of thought describe these governing vital energies
as ki, chi, prana and so on. However, there is one common
component to all these systems of healing. They all believe
that a subtle energy system governs the mind and body.
In their natural undisturbed state, these energies ensure
mental and physical well-being in an individual. If these
energies are disrupted for any reason, say due to trauma,
inappropriate environmental exposure, or incorrect diet,

then physical or mental symptoms of disease are manifested in an individual.

Energy healing aims at correcting what is considered as the root cause — the disruption in the energy system. By restoring balance to subtle energies, mental or physical disease is also healed. Energy healing can be divided into two types.

The first one uses measurable or *veritable* energy fields for healing. These would include discernible energies such as electromagnetism, sound or laser beams.

A large number of healing practices fall into the secondary category, where *putative* energy fields are employed. Putative is defined by the dictionary as, "commonly put forth or accepted as true on inconclusive grounds". Many age-old therapies such as reiki, acupressure, acupuncture, faith healing and intercessory prayer rely on such forces, which science has been unable to measure so far.

It should be noted that *conventional* or *allopathic* medicine has focused its attention on correcting symptoms, while ignoring or refuting any *energy* systems in the background. This was understandable, given the limitations of measuring instruments and scientific knowledge. Physics was still restricted to Newton's laws and our understanding of biology and chemistry was far more limited than it is now. Today's scientists are changing their mindsets. Newtonian mechanics can explain matter at the macroscopic level. However, these laws do not stand at subatomic levels of measurement. The evolution of quantum physics, sophisticated measuring and diagnostic tools, developments in molecular biology, biochemistry, genetics and epigenetics lead scientists to revise their hypothesis and understanding each day.

The mystery of the intricate functioning of the mind and body is yet to be understood completely. Nevertheless, the standards set up by Western medicine have useful merit. Empirical testing, safety and efficacy of any form of healing are desirable. Do not forget, that despite this, significant adverse drug or treatment reactions do occur frequently, even in conventional medicine. Regardless of stringent systems for testing and approval, many drugs have had to be recalled or have proven dangerous in the real world. After all, testing and trials have their own physical and commercial limitations.

Traditional medicine using putative energy fields have a lot of anecdotal testimonials that contribute towards their widespread acceptance. Some of them, such as acupuncture, have been in use for thousands of years. Proving many of these systems under *scientific guidelines* has been difficult because the treatment is usually customised to an individual's need and is often incapable of being standardised.

However, a few studies done on acupuncture have shown perceptible results. Research is also being done to validate EFT results as per contemporary, orthodox requirements. But these are still early days and few studies have been completed so far.

3.2: What is EFT?

EFT is a set of techniques that has demonstrated success with personal improvement, as well as physical and emotional healing in hundreds of individuals. We use the plural term techniques, as over the years, several variants of the original protocol have gained in popularity. EFT is based on the ancient system of acupuncture, but does not involve any needles or invasive techniques. There is also no ingestion or exposure to any foreign substance.

Acupuncture is based on the belief that the well-being of the mind and body is governed by a set of energy meridians and stimulating certain points along these meridians can restore a person's health. EFT involves stimulating a select few of these points, by tapping with our fingertips. Accompanying statements or affirmations aim to address a specific issue. These statements play an important role, alongside the tapping, as they generally encourage a person to accept a problem or situation as it currently stands, and then to move towards its resolution.

EFT was founded by Gary Craig, a Stanford engineer, performance coach, Neuro Linguistic Programming (NLP) Master Practitioner and Ordained Minister. He developed this technique on the basis of earlier work done by Dr Roger Callahan, a clinical psychologist. Gary Craig brought in the 100 per cent overhaul concept used in engineering, in order to arrive at a simple and standardised procedure. The concept implies that tapping on several key points will restore the *default* setting in meridians which are disturbed and simply *service* those which do not necessarily need any work. Hence, the same protocol can be used on a wide variety of issues with success. Standardising the procedure and that too to a limited set of stimulation points, has enabled people to learn and teach EFT within minutes. EFT can be understood, experimented with and taught to others with great ease and speed.

As the name suggests, EFT was originally used for seeking freedom from negative emotions. Fears, phobias, anxiety, depression, stress, anger, resentment and many other such issues were addressed and dealt with successfully.

Over a period of time, it was observed that healing emotional issues, often led to relief from physical disease as well. Of course, proponents of the mind-body connection would have little difficulty in explaining such an effect. Our emotions cause a cascade of chemical and physiological changes in our body. A constant exposure to the consequences of negative emotions can be expected to lead to physical issues. Subsequently, EFT was tried on a variety of physical ailments and people have frequently found that EFT often works, where nothing else will.

3.3: Why EFT?

There are many advantages of EFT. Some of these are:

Works even if you are skeptical: Many first time users ask if it is necessary to 'believe in EFT' or have some kind of faith in it, for it to work. Despite doubts or disbelief, do try a few rounds of EFT for yourself. The results will speak for themselves.

You cannot go wrong with the procedure: EFT is highly flexible and many variants of it have developed over the years. You can describe issues as they stand, or in the way you would like them to be. You can incorporate some extra tapping or neglect some points, as is done in the short-cut technique. You will generally see positive results.

You can state the problem as it stands: The popular use of positive affirmations is a technique to change negative self-talk into something more positive, by constant repetition of a positive statement. However, positive affirmations involve some stringent rules to formulating an affirmation, such as use of only positive words, present tense, etc. With EFT, you have the advantage of stating things as they stand. This rings true for most people as they find it easier to start with a statement that they can resonate with. For instance, saying, "I am happy and joyous right now", when you are actually feeling depressed, is rather difficult and pointless for many people. With EFT, you would start with, "Even though I am feeling depressed..."and move on from there.

You can get a lot done on your own: EFT is an empowering tool that you are encouraged to use by yourself, on a routine basis. While it would be advisable and beneficial to seek professional help with the more complex or serious issues, there are many areas where you are likely to make significant progress, in spite of working alone.

Can be done almost anywhere, at anytime: A single round of the full version of EFT (the full basic recipe), takes about a minute. The short-cut version takes about thirty to forty seconds! As you do not require any special tools or setting, you can practice it whenever you feel the need. Utilise the time generally lost during commuting, in waiting rooms and queues, etc. You can even tap while bathing or walking. As long as you do not mind some curious stares or comments, you can tap anywhere you feel like. However, setting aside a proper slot in your daily routine is highly recommended.

Sometimes one or two rounds clear the problem permanently: When this happens, you may never have to work on the same issue again and can move on to the next problem.

Benefits may extend to *untapped* issues: Contrary to the potential adverse side effects of orthodox medicine, EFT often provides additional relief for issues different from the one you have tapped on.

Try it on everything: Innovative uses are being discovered every day, as people experiment with EFT in a variety of ways, and within different application areas.

Can be used for others, even over a distance: Remember, we are dealing with energy healing. Just as a television signal can be broadcast over space, EFT benefits have been experienced over geographical distances. See 'Proxy or Surrogate Tapping' for more details.

3.4: Will EFT interfere with my other treatment or techniques?

EFT is a highly complementary technique and does not interfere with any other system of healing, orthodox medicine or personal improvement. In fact, it is likely that you will be able to use EFT to enhance the results you are obtaining from any other plan you are following. Energy healers are likely to see faster, improved results. For instance, reiki channels will probably notice an immediate increase in the flow of reiki.

Those using EFT for health purposes are advised to monitor their tests carefully and more frequently, as medicine and treatment may require tapering adjustments, which should be made by the qualified health care provider.

3.5: What should one expect after a round of EFT?

- Some people feel drowsy and may want to take a nap. Many people feel fresh and energetic instead. It will depend on your individual condition.

- You may experience various 'body sounds', such as yawning, burping or stomach growls. This is often indicative of a clearing of the energy disruption.

- You may have a sudden insight into the root cause of the apparent problem, or a better understanding of the situation from a different perspective.

- Over a period of time, you should be able to observe subtle changes in your self and situation.

- The intensity of the issue may fade away completely and a new emotion or *aspect* may take up your attention. Physical symptoms, for example pain may shift location or change in quality. You may address this new *aspect* with a fresh round of EFT.

- A sudden lack of intensity or complete absence of the problem being tapped upon often leaves people surprised and they may attribute this to any factor other than EFT, for example "I was distracted" or "It was not that important anyway." This phenomenon is frequently observed during EFT sessions and is referred to as the apex effect.

- EFT is quite gentle and rarely has any serious side effects. In rare cases, there may be abreactions, a temporary aggravation of symptoms or mild nausea. If there is any discomfort, continuing to tap a few more rounds usually results in relief. However, please ensure that you have read the 'Terms of Use' and have taken appropriate precautions.

3.6: How frequently can I use EFT in a day?

Ideally, try to use EFT at least one to three times a day. Using it daily not only has obvious benefits on the issues being tapped on, but side-benefits begin to accrue as well. Additionally, you will always remember that you have this versatile and useful knowledge and are more likely to use it, when confronted with sudden or severe challenges.

There does not appear to be any upper limit to the number of times that one can use EFT — one cannot *overdose* on it. In fact, people using it for long-standing issues or chronic disease, have been known to resort to EFT for several hours a day, as they have numerous and severe challenges to overcome. Note that it is important to drink plenty of water when you use EFT, especially with frequent usage.

3.7: How can one benefit from EFT?

Application of EFT is only limited by our imagination. Several specific areas of application and relevant suggestions are listed separately in this book. However, as stated earlier, 'try it on everything'. Whenever you find yourself grappling with a problem, you should consider trying EFT.

Not only can you use it to solve past or chronic issues, but you can also use EFT for affirming your intentions, instilling and enhancing positive traits and for developing more positive and productive qualities in your self and in your life. For example, use EFT on a daily basis, in the morning, to intend a positive and productive day. At the end of the day, you can use it to relax yourself and release emotional and physical tensions that you faced during the day.

In addition to being a tool of continuous improvement and growth, EFT can also be used as a *first-aid* measure. Obviously, all sensible measures should also be taken concurrently, but EFT can be administered while you are waiting for qualified help. It may also make sense to try EFT, before you try anything else that poses graver risks.

Newcomers to EFT frequently obtain a great deal of success with it. However, to secure enduring and long-term benefits, the objective viewpoint, compassionate support and extensive knowledge and experience of a practitioner may be required. One-on-one sessions are detailed and exhaustive. Sometimes, several hours of work, spread over several sittings, may be required to address the more long-standing or challenging issues. Each of us has a lot of emotional baggage and how much you are committed to working on yourself, will determine the extent of use that you make of such self-improvement techniques.

4 | Getting Started

"The world is moving so fast these days that the man who says it can't be done is generally interrupted by someone doing it."

— **Harry Emerson Fosdick**

Aishwariya was a student who had a long history of exam anxiety. All her life, she would develop extreme nervousness and panic on the day before her paper. This invariably affected her ability to translate her hard work into academic performance. On the day before her first Masters paper, she came to me in a complete nervous state. She was sure that she would be completely *blank* during her paper and rated her Subjective Units of Disturbance (SUD) level as nine, indicating complete panic. She was speaking loudly, in a high pitch and was breathing shallowly. She was sceptical about EFT calming her as exam anxiety was a long-standing challenge for her.

Nevertheless, as suggested, she started tapping with, "Even though I am afraid I will go blank during the paper,

I deeply and completely love, forgive and accept myself." After two rapid rounds of short-cut technique, we changed the set-up to, "Even though I am still panicking, I deeply and completely love, forgive and accept myself". I asked her to repeat two rounds of tapping. Her breathing settled and her voice calmed. She looked visibly relaxed. Her fresh evaluation of SUD was now three. I asked her to tap another two rounds using, "Even though I am still a little nervous about my paper, I choose to be calm now." At the end of two rounds, her SUDs were zero. She was calm and delighted with the change. I recommended that she continue tapping a round using, "I choose to be calm", if she felt any anxiety coming back.

After her exams, she reported that she had effectively calmed herself down every time she started getting anxious and had cleared all her papers with ease.

This chapter outlines short-cut EFT technique. Out of the many variants of EFT that have developed over the years, this is possibly one of the most popular and widely used protocols.

Before we begin the exercise, a few important reminders:

- Avoid tapping directly after a heavy meal.
- Drink water. EFT tends to increase thirst and if you are dehydrated, you may not see satisfactory results.
- Avoid crossing your legs or ankles when you are tapping for your self.
- It is always a good idea to begin by stating the intention that the results will be in 'your highest good'.

The EFT short-cut can be summarised as follows:

1. Test for SUD on a scale of one to ten.

2. Set-up the affirmation.

3. Tap a sequence of eight points while repeating the reminder phrase, as detailed below.

4. Test your SUD again.

5. If your SUD is not zero, then modify your set-up and reminder phrases suitably and repeat steps two to four until your SUD drops to zero or you are satisfied with the outcome.

It is that simple!

Detailed description of the short-cut technique:

1. **Checking SUD levels:** SUD levels refer to the value that you assign to your issue, on a scale of one to ten, which acts as an indicator of the current intensity being experienced. Close your eyes, take a deep breath, release and focus on your issue. Now evaluate the intensity and assign a number from one to ten.

   For example, if you are suffering from a migraine, an intense unbearable pain, accompanied by sensitivity to light, may warrant a nine. Our aim will be to try for a completely pain free state, which would imply a SUD of zero.

   Similarly, suppose you have to address an audience and are experiencing stage fright. If possible, identify one particular symptom of this anxiety, say your trembling hands, otherwise try to rate the general feeling of anxiety itself. For example, if your hands are visibly shaking uncontrollably, then this may be well measured by an eight. Whereas being completely calm would be reflected by a zero.

SUD by definition, is naturally *subjective*, as it does not involve any specific measurements. It is completely dependent on your evaluation of the situation. We use SUD levels to gauge our progress and the trend is more important than getting the figure exactly right. So don't stress yourself over whether your initial level should be a seven or eight. Go with your first guess and that should work fine.

2. **Set-up your affirmation:** Detailed assistance on framing your own affirmations is provided in other chapters. For the purpose of simplicity, at this juncture, you may use the following fill in the blank phrase to frame your affirmation: "Even though I have this _____, I deeply and completely love, forgive and accept myself."

This phrase has been used with great success for a variety of issues. So if you get stuck with framing your own set-up or simply would like a default option, go ahead and use this one.

To go back to our earlier examples of an intense headache, or stage fright, the corresponding set-up affirmations would read:

"Even though I have this *intense headache*, I deeply and completely love, forgive and accept myself."

"Even though *the stage fright is making my hands shake*, I deeply and completely love, forgive and accept myself."

The problem or issue used to fill in the blank will be your reminder phrase, which we will use in step three.

(The italicised portion will indicate the reminder phrase in examples throughout the rest of the book).

Now that you have formulated your set-up and reminder phrases, you begin your EFT by repeating the entire set-up affirmation (as long as it may be!) three times, all the time tapping on your Karate Chop (KC) point. The KC point is the fleshy part of the side of your hand that you would normally hit, if attempting a karate chop. You tap it with your other open palm, or with four fingertips hitting the side of your hand as shown in the photograph. You can also tap your KC by hitting a table top with *light* karate chops. The pressure should be firm, yet gentle. Do not hurt yourself!

Tapping at all points, including the KC point, can be done with either hand. You may switch sides during the tapping, or even use both hands for the remaining points. As stated before, EFT is very flexible and you really cannot do anything *wrong*.

3. **Tapping sequence:** Using your index and middle fingertips, tap gently, but firmly, five to seven times on each of the points given below as shown in the visuals. Remember to repeat the reminder phrase once at each of these points, as you tap.

   a. Eyebrow point or EB is located just below and inside the inner starting edge of your eyebrow.

   b. Side of the Eye or SE is the bony part of your eye socket adjacent to the outer edge of your eye.

   c. Under the Eye or UE is located below the centre of your eye. Here too, you will feel the bony edge of your eye socket.

d. Under the Nose or UN is the area between your nose and upper lip.

e. Chin or CH refers to the indented area just below your lower lip.

f. Collarbone or CB actually refers to the end of the collarbone, to the immediate left and right of the hollow at the base of your throat.

g. Under the Arm or UA is the area on your side, about three to four inches below your armpit, in line with your breast.

h. Crown of the Head or CRH is located at the apex of your skull, half way between an imaginary line

Karate Chop point

Step 3a, Eyebrow point

Step 3b, Side of the Eye point

Step 3c, Under the Eye point

Step 3d, Under the Nose point

Step 3e, Chin point

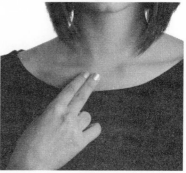

Step 3f, Collarbone point

Step 3g, Under the Arm point   Step 3h, Crown of the Head point

joining the two ears. It is sometimes referred to as Top of the Head or TH. You can tap here with all your fingertips, in small circular movements. Be particularly gentle at this point. This point is sometimes omitted in the short-cut method. Also note that it is not included in the full basic recipe or long form.

Whenever possible, tap on both sides. Familiarise yourself with the abbreviations of these points as given above, as these abbreviations are used throughout the book as well as in other books, articles or websites on EFT.

4. **Test SUD again:** Take a deep breath, release and now re-evaluate. You need to check as to whether you have made any headway at all, and if yes, to what extent.

If you feel there is no change in your SUD, then try repeating steps two and three once more. If you still feel there is *no difference whatsoever* (a rare occurrence), then please see the chapter on 'When You are Not Seeing Results.'

5. **If your SUD is now less than original, tap again, with modification:** If you find that the intensity of your issue has decreased, even marginally, say by 0.5 or one, or more, but has not yet become zero, then modify your set-up affirmation and reminder phrases in the following way:

"Even though I *still* have this _____, I deeply and completely love, forgive and accept myself."

Use *"remaining_____* as your reminder phrase during the tapping sequence.

Corresponding changes for the examples would be:

"Even though I *still* have this *intense headache*, I deeply and completely love, forgive and accept myself."

Here the reminder phrase is *"remaining intense headache."*

"Even though *the stage fright is still making my hands shake*, I deeply and completely love, forgive and accept myself."

Here the reminder phrase is *"remaining stage-fright"* or *"remaining shaking hands."*

Continue the same cycle of testing, set-up, tapping and re-evaluating until your SUD drops to zero or you are satisfied with the result. Generally, there is a small, but noticeable decrease in the first round itself, with increasing drops in the subsequent rounds. Long-standing or highly serious issues may require five to seven rounds, but in most cases, satisfactory results are obtained within a few rounds. As each short-cut round takes about thirty to forty seconds, sometimes the quick results make EFT seem almost magical.

Now that you are familiar with the short-cut technique, try the following exercises.

Exercise One: To energise yourself or decrease fatigue.

Step one: Close your eyes and take a deep breath and release. Rate how tired you are feeling right now. Fresh and energetic would mean a SUD of zero and there is no point in you trying this now! Perhaps you would prefer to try the next exercise. However, if you are feeling completely drained, and cannot lift a finger, then that would be a ten. Most people would pick a number between four and seven.

Step two: Repeat the following sentence thrice, while tapping your KC: "Even though I am feeling quite tired right now, I would rather feel energetic."

Notice how differently I have framed the set-up. I could have easily used the default statement given earlier, but since I am looking for a specific result — to feel energised, I have framed it accordingly.

Step three: Tap five to seven times on each of the remaining eight points described above, repeating "feeling quite tired" once at each point.

Step four: Take a deep breath and release. Re-evaluate your SUD. It would probably have lowered by one or two.

Step five: Repeat the following statement three times, while tapping your KC: "Even though I am still feeling tired right now, I would rather feel energetic."

Step six: Tap five to seven times on each of the remaining eight points described above, repeating "still feeling tired" once at each point.

Step seven: Take a deep breath and release. Re-evaluate your SUD. Are you feeling more energetic? If you want, you can continue this cycle a few more times.

Exercise Two: To improve breathing.

This is a good experiment for those who would like to try EFT, but are not experiencing any symptoms at the present moment. In modern, stressed and hectic times, most of us do not breathe as properly, as we should. This exercise aims at improving your oxygenation. You will have to be a little more attentive whilst measuring your SUD levels, as what we are estimating is more subtle than active symptoms.

Step one: Close your eyes and breathe in deeply, then release. Repeat this twice. This is to exercise your lungs and make you more conscious of the amount of air that you are taking in. Now take in a more comfortable breath, that is do not make any special effort at breathing in large amounts of air. If you can, imagine the air entering your lungs, filling up from the bottom, towards the top. Now try to estimate or guess at how much air you have filled in, on a scale of one to ten. For example, if your lungs feel full, the number would be ten, but this would be an exceptional case. Only the most fit people are likely to feel that way. More commonly, it is probably between six to eight. I am assuming a seven for simplicity here. Accordingly, your SUD level will be 10 – 7, that is 3. (10 – 7, because we are attempting to rate the units of *disturbance*, not comfort).

Step two: Repeat the following sentence thrice, while tapping your KC: "Even though I am not breathing in fully, I would rather experience better oxygenation now."

Again, please note that the default statement is not used here though that too could have been used instead.

Step three: Tap five to seven times on each of the remaining eight points described above, repeating "not breathing in fully" once at each point.

Step four: Take a breath and release. Re-evaluate your SUD. It would probably have lowered marginally. It may be harder to distinguish a result in this exercise, so go on to the next step.

Step five: Repeat the following words three times, while tapping your KC: "Even though I am still not breathing in fully, I would rather experience better oxygenation now."

Step six: Tap five to seven times on each of the remaining eight points described above, repeating "still not breathing in fully" once at each point.

Step seven: Take a breath and release. Re-evaluate your SUD. Do you notice a difference now? If you want, you can continue this cycle a few more times. Within two or three rounds of this exercise, most people will notice improved breathing and more energy.

5 | The Choices Trio

"Your living is determined not so much by what life brings to you as by the attitude you bring to life; not so much by what happens to you as by the way your mind looks at what happens."

— **Kahlil Gibran**

Tanuja was a thirty-five-year-old who lost her husband in sudden and tragic circumstances. Overwhelmed by grief and depression, she was struggling with her loss. The choices trio played a significant role in her turnaround and was arrived at as follows:

Tanuja attempted to describe her husband and their happy marriage, but was unable to continue due to her intense grief. She bit her lips and tried to contain the tears that were flowing down her cheeks. She kept shaking her head and muttering, "I miss him a lot". Clearly, her SUD could be rated as ten. I asked her to start tapping on her KC with the set-up, "Even though I miss him a lot, I love, forgive and accept myself." We tapped three short-cut rounds using "*miss him a lot*" as the reminder phrase. After this she had stopped crying and was a little calmer. She said her SUD was now seven. Tanuja said, "All I can think of is that he is not there anymore! I can't think beyond that!"

I asked her to recollect the happiest time they had together, all the while tapping on her KC point. She brightened slightly as she began to describe a vacation they had taken last summer. She reported the vacation in great detail and as she spoke, she began to smile fondly. Tanuja paused in her story and with clear eyes declared, "Even if he is gone, I would rather remember the good times happily, than keep crying over what I have lost." At this point, I suggested that it would be extremely useful for her to use this approach with the choices trio. Accordingly, we framed her choices set-up as: "Even though *I miss him a lot*, I am grateful for the summer vacation we had." I told her to visualise the vacation and all the positive feelings she had at its mention, whilst tapping. After two rounds of the choices trio, she was calm and relaxed, with a smile on her face.

Naturally, the loss of a dear one can never be replaced or forgotten. But instead of being depressed and disconsolate over the death (which after all is a true, inevitable reality of life) of her husband Tanuja found a way to focus on her appreciation for the time they had shared together. She has continued to use this particular method on a frequent basis and reports that it always makes her more positive, happy and grateful for the good times she shared with her husband.

After EFT consultations, she was equipped with a tool that helped her cope with the tragedy in a far healthier manner. She has regained her strength and joy for life and is now able to work and look after her self and her child with loving care and attention.

No matter what the situation is, how you *respond* to it is always up to you. Your instinctive reactions may be determined by several factors such as conditioning, past experience or your belief system. Frequently, fatigue contributes towards disheartened and hopeless *reactions*. Instead of this, exercise your choice on what attitude to adopt. Consciously deciding on a more appropriate response is empowering and generates a more constructive mindset and action plan.

Incorporating the use of the words "I choose" in your EFT set-up serves a dual purpose. First, there is an implicit acceptance that your current attitude or situation is not the way you would like it to be. This ensures that you are being realistic, without expending energies on denial, pessimism or fake optimism. Secondly, whatever choice you incorporate into this framework, it is more likely to energise and motivate you. Your sense of helplessness or victimised feelings would be converted into an affirmative and positive attitude. Adding the word *now* or *instead* at the end of your choice can emphasise this significant shift of attitude and bring a sense of awareness, importance and urgency to the fresh choice you are making.

Consider the following example: You feel shy and awkward meeting new people, but would rather come across as confident and self-assured. There are four different ways in which one could frame an EFT set-up statement for this situation:

- Even though I feel shy and awkward meeting new people, *I deeply and completely love, forgive and accept myself.*

- Even though I feel shy and awkward meeting new people, *I choose to be confident and self-assured now.*

- Even though I feel shy and awkward meeting new people, *I intend to be confident and self-assured instead.*

- Even though I feel shy and awkward meeting new people, *I would rather be confident and self-assured.*

To keep focus on the *choice* factor, I have only made changes in the positive part of the set-up. At first glance, these may all appear to be similar. But, depending on your frame of mind and the extent to which you are comfortable assuming responsibility for yourself, one of these will appear more acceptable or attractive to you than the others.

Naturally, use of such affirmations should be restricted to choices which are yours to make. By that, I mean that you are not expected to make choices on behalf of others. Each individual should be allowed to exercise his own free will and no matter how well intentioned your ideas may be, they are still *your* choices, and may not necessarily be the same as his. Even if you feel that the affirmation can have only a positive impact, or you have the requisite responsibility or authority (e.g. as parent or caregiver), I advocate the incorporation of a tag, "If this is in the highest good."

Once you have framed or selected your set-up, you can use the short-cut method or the full basic recipe described in the following chapter.

But as this chapter is all about the many choices that you can make, here is another excellent option, developed by Dr Patricia Carrington (PhD), a proficient and world renowned EFT Master Practitioner. Dr Carrington has kindly given her permission for me to share her 'The Choices Trio' EFT method in this book.

The choices trio can be briefly summarised as follows:

1. Check your SUD level for the negative component you are tapping for.

2. Repeat your entire set-up statement three times, while tapping your Karate Chop point. (e.g. entire statement one, "Even though I feel shy and awkward meeting new people, I deeply and completely love, forgive and accept myself.")

3. Tapping round one: Repeat the negative component (e.g. "shy and awkward meeting new people") while tapping at each of the tapping points in the short-cut method at:

   a. EB
   b. SE
   c. UE
   d. UN
   e. CH
   f. CB
   g. UA
   h. CRH

4. Tapping round second: Repeat the positive component (e.g. "I choose to be confident and self-assured now") while tapping at each of the tapping points in the short-cut method at:

   a. EB
   b. SE
   c. UE

     d.   UN

     e.   CH

     f.   CB

     g.   UA

     h.   CRH

5. Tapping round third: Tap on each of the EFT spots, alternating negative and positive phrases — as per the example:

     a.   EB: "shy and awkward meeting new people."

     b.   SE: "I choose to be confident and self-assured now."

     c.   UE: "shy and awkward meeting new people."

     d.   UN: "I choose to be confident and self-assured now."

     e.   CH: "shy and awkward meeting new people."

     f.   CB: "I choose to be confident and self-assured now."

     g.   UA: "shy and awkward meeting new people."

     h.   CRH: "I choose to be confident and self-assured now."

6. Check your SUD.

7. If required, repeat steps two to six.

Note: Dr Carrington uses CRH only in tapping round third. However, I prefer to use it throughout, as described earlier.

Though tapping rounds one and two give noticeable results by themselves, the idea of alternating negative and positive in the third round proves to be very useful in restructuring your mental associations. By repeatedly following the negative with a positive, this round effectively retrains your mind to automatically substitute the negative thought with your positive choice instead. Hence, this is more efficient than attempting to eliminate an undesirable, as you are replacing it with a more desirable attitude or state.

The choices trio is particularly effective in:

- Instilling positive traits, such as confidence, friendliness, dynamism, enthusiasm, etc.
- Establishing positive and healthy habits, such as exercise routines, punctuality, organised approach, etc.
- Changing instinctive reactions to considered responses.

Some sample set-up statements for the choices trio:

- Even though I am afraid of public speaking, I choose to deliver my presentations with remarkable poise.
- Even though I am afraid to speak up for myself, I choose to firmly assert myself when required.
- Even though I am very forgetful, I choose to have a photographic memory instead.
- Even though I tend to procrastinate till the last possible minute, I choose to meet my deadlines with ease.
- Even though I am highly disorganised, I choose to plan and execute tasks efficiently now.
- Even though I am terrified of ___, I choose to be calm and composed now.

- Even though I hate going to work on Mondays, I intend to be fresh and enthusiastic instead.

- Even though I avoid going to the gym, I intend to enjoy my exercise routine now.

- Even though X tests my patience, I intend to be tolerant and patient.

- Even though I feel this situation is hopeless, I intend to find a creative and innovative solution.

- Even though X's inefficiency infuriates me, I would rather deal with X calmly and appropriately.

- Even though I feel justified in hating X, I would rather choose peace instead.

- Even though I am always late for work, I would rather demonstrate impressive punctuality instead.

- Even though I am anxious about my test results, I would rather anticipate them with optimism.

- Even though I tend to spend carelessly, I would rather be thrifty now.

6 | The Full Basic Recipe

"If you can imagine it you can create it. If you can dream it, you can become it."
— **William Ward**

Radhika is an independent thirty-year-old who ran away from home at the age of eighteen. She had endured repeated abuse and incest, at the hands of her father and brothers from a very early age. Such cases are unfortunately neither rare, nor restricted to any particular strata of society. As any discussion on this subject is considered a taboo very little support is available to many such victims, who often experience guilt and shame for no fault of theirs.

In her first EFT session, Radhika bravely recounted her entire history. The first aspect that clearly emerged was that though she logically understood that she was in no way responsible for all that she had endured, there was an internal voice that said "maybe I invited this" and "I can't love myself". She also reported a variety of physical symptoms for which no diagnosis could be established and confessed to being a heavy smoker.

Due to the high intensity of history, emotions and many aspects involved, I suggested that she use the full basic recipe. For the first session, we decided to stay focused on her father. Starting with a SUD level of seven for her guilt, she started tapping with, "Even though I feel I may have invited my father's abuse, I know that I was only an innocent child." With tightness in her chest and a clenched jaw, she began tapping determinedly. As she progressed through the gamut procedure, there was a visible relaxation on her face. At the end of first round she let out a couple of deep exhalations and sighed. She said that, "Though I have known this all the time, for once I feel like I may be able to believe it!" I asked her to tap some more full basic recipe rounds, changing over to, "Even though I felt like I was responsible for the abuse, I realise I was helpless at that time", followed by, "Even though I have felt guilty all this time, I am proud of how I have looked after myself for the last twelve years." At the end of half an hour, Radhika was completely at peace on this aspect and had succeeded in bringing down her SUD to zero.

Thanks to her innate strength and commitment to self-help, she remains a dedicated tapper and has been consistently working on all her issues for a couple of months now. Radhika grows stronger and more compassionate with herself and others everyday. She has actually been able to forgive her father and brothers and is attempting to reconnect with her family. She is now completely at ease with, "loving and accepting herself". Her physical health has been improving and she has quit smoking. Awed by the benefits she has had from EFT, she is currently undergoing training to become an EFT practitioner herself.

At this point, you should be well familiar with the short-cut method described in 'Getting Started'. The full basic recipe was actually the original form of EFT, but is a little more elaborate. Nevertheless, it still takes little over a minute to complete one round. There are three major differences between the short-cut method and the full basic recipe technique:

- There are two rounds of tapping instead of one.

- Instead of using the CRH point, four additional tapping points on the hand, as well as the KC point are used in each tapping round. All the four additional tapping points are located on the side of the finger (the inner side closer to your body), just in line with the beginning of the nail (see photographs). The reminder phrase is repeated at all these points as well.

- The 9 gamut procedure is followed in between the two tapping rounds. The gamut point is located just above the midpoint of the knuckle between the little and ring finger (see photograph). Whilst tapping this point, do the following:

  - Close your eyes.

  - Open your eyes.

  - Look down and towards the right, keeping the head steady.

  - Look down and towards the left, keeping the head steady.

  - Roll your eyes in a full clockwise circle.

  - Roll your eyes in an anticlockwise circle.

  - Hum any song for two seconds.

- Count rapidly from one to five.

- Hum the song again for two seconds.

The gamut procedure is frequently amusing to first time users. However, it serves a purpose. The eye movements are intended to activate various parts of the brain and the alternate humming and counting activate usage in the right and left hemispheres. Use of the gamut and the full basic recipe is specially recommended for people who began to walk early and did not crawl enough as babies. The gamut procedure is also relevant in issues involving brain injury or neurological disease, allergies, and compromised immunity, as well as intense emotional issues. The 9 gamut works on 'The Triple Warmer' meridian, which is considered to be one of the important acupuncture meridians.

I suggest using the full basic recipe at least once a day, whilst those having serious or chronic issues should stick to the full basic recipe as frequently as possible.

The following steps summarise the full basic recipe:

1. Test for SUD on a scale of one to ten.

2. Set-up the affirmation by repeating it three times while tapping at the Karate Chop or KC point.

3. In the first round of tapping, repeat the reminder phrase and tap five to seven times at each of the twelve points detailed below:

    a. Eyebrow point or EB is located just below and inside the inner starting edge of your eyebrow.

    b. Side of the Eye or SE is the bony part of your eye socket adjacent to the outer edge of your eye.

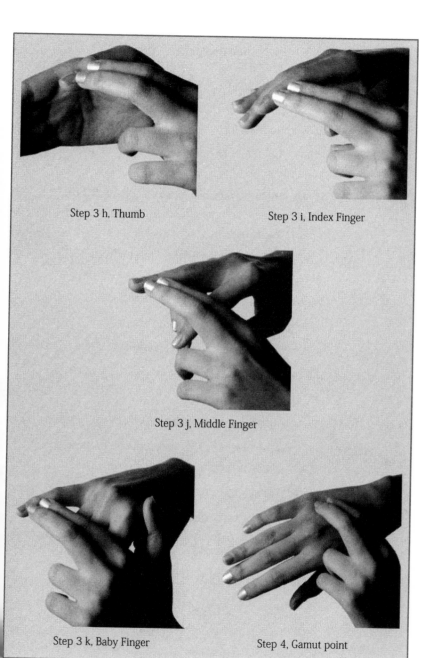

Step 3 h, Thumb

Step 3 i, Index Finger

Step 3 j, Middle Finger

Step 3 k, Baby Finger

Step 4, Gamut point

c. Under the Eye or UE is located below the centre of your eye. Here too, you will feel the bony edge of your eye socket.

d. Under the Nose or UN is the area between your nose and upper lip.

e. Chin or CH refers to the indented area just below your lower lip.

f. Collarbone or CB actually refers to the *end* of the collarbone, to the immediate left and right of the hollow at the base of your throat.

g. Under the Arm or UA is the area on your side, about three to four inches below your armpit.

h. Side of the Thumb or Th, near base of nail.

i. Side of Index Finger or IF, near base of nail.

j. Side of Middle Finger or MF, near base of nail.

k. Side of Baby/little Finger or BF, near base of nail.

l. KC point.

4. Do the 9 gamut procedure as described above.

5. Tapping round second: This is identical to taping round one of twelve points described above.

6. Test your SUD again.

7. If your SUD is not zero, then modify your set-up and reminder phrases to focus on the 'remaining issue' and repeat steps two to six until your SUD drops to zero or you are satisfied with the outcome.

7 | General Guidelines for Framing Set-ups and Reminder Phrases

"Creativity is allowing yourself to make mistakes. Art is knowing which ones to keep."

— **Scott Adams**

The set-up affirmation or statement and the corresponding reminder phrase used in any of the EFT methods play an important part. The mechanical tapping works towards restoring balance to the disrupted energy system and hence some healing benefit will accrue from tapping alone. This may be the possible explanation for *side-benefits* that are frequently experienced with EFT. Side-benefits refer to improvements and healing in issues other than those being addressed during the tapping.

However, the set-up and reminder phrase define your current priority or pressing need and prioritise the healing towards this urgent matter. Consider this analogy: You are in a huge mansion, on the first floor, in the fifth bedroom. Something disrupts the electrical circuits and only the lights in your room go out. Let us assume that you immediately call for an electrician. What would you say to him? You could simply tell him to check the entire mansion and start work on correcting each and every thing that is wrong in the electric circuit. Of course, then you would end up waiting in the darkness, until he finally reaches your room and fixes the particular problem. So it's more likely that you will tell him to first, "fix the lights in the fifth room on the first floor" and then have him service the rest of the mansion. Correct? Similarly, your set-up statements and reminder phrases focus correction of the energy disruption and healing on the matter that is most important to you at that particular point.

Investing some time and effort in framing your set-ups and reminders can help you obtain results quickly. Here are some guidelines to help you in this regard:

Default set-up and reminder phrase: "Even though I have this _____, I deeply and completely love, forgive and accept myself."

We use the keywords placed in the blank as the reminder phrase. Several reasons make this a good default set-up. Firstly, very few people are habituated to genuinely loving, forgiving or accepting themselves. Imagine this scenario: You are the proud new owner of the latest, most expensive car in the market. You generously lend it to someone dear and close to you. This person takes the car for a spin and crashes it, while he remains unhurt. What is your very first instinctive reaction?

Most of the responses would be like, "Thank God he is safe!" Of course, anger, despair, etc. may follow shortly thereafter. But if you were the driver yourself and the car meets with an accident, your centre of attention would be the damage done to the vehicle and the related cost, rather than gratitude for your good fortune. Don't you think that you should have the same sentiment of love, forgiveness and acceptance for yourself as you would for any body else?

If you have difficulty in using the statement, then identify why you are reluctant to say "love/forgive/accept myself" and first tap for that. Here itself, you may discover hidden self-esteem issues or negative thinking patterns.

This is a versatile sentence that can easily be adapted for use with most issues. For example, you could use: "Even though I cannot forgive myself, I deeply and completely love, forgive and accept myself *anyway!*" or "Even though I cannot forgive myself, *let me try* to love, forgive and accept myself!"

Last, but not the least, this set-up has worked effectively for hundreds of issues. Consequently, it offers itself as the obvious starting point.

Being specific: It is usually helpful and often gives faster results. So identify each emotion, issue or *aspect* and work on them separately. Try to be precise and specific in description as well. If your left knee is throbbing, then use "throbbing pain in my left knee" instead of just *pain* or *knee trouble.*

A generalised emotion or belief regarding a person or situation is well addressed by dealing with specific events, one at a time. For example, if you feel your father does not love you and has never approved of you, instead of tapping on "Even though my father never loved me…", try to recollect three or four specific events which are demonstrative of this belief. Choose events that trigger an intense reaction and tap on the different aspects and emotions that they invoke in you. It does not matter if in hindsight, your logic tells you that this was an unimportant event or there was some explanation or justification for your father's behaviour. The point is that your negative emotions were triggered and so this event is still an issue for you. So suppose you remember being hugely disappointed because he never turned up for your sixth birthday party, or he never praised you for winning the 500 metre race in grade seven, etc. It is a combination of several such events that leads to beliefs such as "my father never loved me" or "my father never cared for me." Generally, working on three to five such events, allows one to make significant progress and is likely to result in dissolving these beliefs or the intense emotions. However, some persistent cases may require a little longer time. Still, don't worry, it's not as though you are required to tap on every single one of the hundreds of such interactions you would have had with your father!

Try to stay focused on the same aspect and collapse each issue before moving to a different emotion or issue. For example, if you are furious with your boss for keeping you late at work, but are also afraid that you are never going to finish the project on time, then work on say anger first, bring SUD to zero and then tap for the fear.

Bundling issues: There are some cases, where being specific is too painful or too traumatic for an individual. If one tries to recall abuse or a tragic accident, it may trigger very high SUD levels, making the person highly disturbed. In such cases, it can be helpful to first do several rounds on *bundled* aspects or emotions, without going into the specific details. Use a metaphor such as a trunk or box and imagine that all the aspects or emotions have been bundled together in it. Alternatively, pick a single keyword that denotes the emotion or event, such as *uncle* or *accident* and first do several rounds using set-ups like:

- "Even though this *box* is deeply disturbing, I choose to let go of it now."

- "Even though this *box* stuff makes me want to clam up/break things/scream, I deeply and completely love, forgive and accept myself."

- "Even though this *uncle* memory (angers/scares/ depresses) me, I give myself permission to heal now."

- "Even though *uncle* makes me (disturbed/confused/ guilty), I would rather be at peace now."

Several such rounds will reduce the intensity until you feel comfortable enough to start addressing the remaining specifics. Subsequently, use EFT to clear up any remaining aspects.

Use the same language and words as in your thoughts: EFT works in any language. The objective is to have you as tuned into your issue as it is possible. For this, using the exact same words is useful, regardless of how objectionable they may be. Be non-judgemental and don't try to justify, deny or moderate your language. Make sure that you use exactly the phrases that come in your head, no matter how rude, ugly or repulsive they may be.

Changing reminder phrase: When in doubt, or when the intensity is too high to allow you to think clearly, let the reminder phrase remain the same throughout the tapping. However, you are free to keep changing the words, as they change with your thoughts.

Continuing the last example, when you are tapping for anger, suppose you start with the following set-up: "Even though *X is a @#!* for keeping me in so late, I would rather be calm and focused now."

Now you may continue using "X is a @#!" at all tapping points, or change it at each point, in keeping with your flow of thoughts: "X always does this", "X is out to get me", "X is ####", "can't stand the sight of him", and so on. Note that all these phrases are related to your anger towards X.

As is where is basis: You may choose to state your problem exactly the way it stands. Adding a positive tailpiece to the issue, as is done in the default statement, helps in moving on from there. Many people find relief in finally being able to state how they feel or think, without any whitewashing or apology. No matter how *unacceptable* it may be, if that is the way you are perceiving things, it is best to acknowledge the situation, without sitting on judgement. We often end up trying to suppress or avoid things which may be unacceptable to society or ourselves, because of conditioning, expectations, etc. The fact of the matter is that denial is very tiring, stressful and pointless. Left unattended and unacknowledged, negative baggage is more likely to cause you harm, rather than disappear! For example, mothers are expected to have an unending supply of love, tolerance, patience, etc. The truth is that every mother is also a human being and may have an occasional *off day*, when her patience and strength do not match the child's requirements. Neither attempting to be the *super mom* (and then helplessly venting your anger and frustration through shouting at or beating the child), nor swallowing your resentments and *suffering silently* is going to achieve any constructive results in the long-term. Instead, a healthier strategy would be acknowledging these emotions in a neutral fashion, healing yourself and letting them go.

I recommend freeing yourself from the negatives first, thereby creating scope to instil positives. For example, telling yourself you are fine, when you are terrified, is likely to sound fake and impossible to you. Instead, you could first tap on, "Even though I am *terrified of* ..." Bring the intensity to zero and then shift to a more positive set-up like: "I choose to be strong and courageous."

However, some people prefer to stick to only positive set-ups and reminders and that works well for them. Do whatever makes you comfortable.

Positive set-ups and reminders: The positive component is always a part of the routine. When you employ 'as is where is basis', notice that you add the positive component as a tail ender in the set-up. You can also use the positive component in isolation, as the set-up and reminder phrases. Common rules of framing positive thinking affirmations apply. Namely, use the present tense and only affirmatives. Avoid negatives like *not* and use the opposite state instead. For example, instead of saying "I am not sick", use, "I am in perfect health and well-being now" or "I experience perfect health and well-being."

- "I choose...", "I intend...", "I will...", and "I am..." are some of the more dynamic ways to frame your affirmations. These phrases lend a sense of purposeful commitment, attitude and action whilst reducing feelings of helplessness or lack of any control over the issue.

- Using words that appeal to you can be more stimulating. For example, "I intend to find an imaginative and innovative solution for this problem," has a stronger impact than a simpler, "I will find a way out of this mess."

You may use the entire set-up as a reminder phrase, or select a single keyword from your set-up.

The choices trio: Substituting negative thoughts or images with positive ones works very well. For example, if you keep recalling a distressing image, say that of a funeral of a dear one, single out another memory of that person that you recall with love and joy. Suppose it was a particular birthday you celebrated together. You could tap on something similar to, "Remembering the *funeral* distresses me, and I would rather remember *birthday* instead." The choices trio is the most appropriate tapping method for such substitution. Visualise the corresponding image mentally, when you use *funeral* and *birthday* as the reminder phrases.

You can also make up the cue that you use as a substitute. Say you are worked up over an interview you are going for and keep imagining how it can go wrong. Visualise (as lucidly as possible) being confident and impressive and having a successful interview. Now tap for, "Even though I am stressed out over *interview,* I intend to have a *success.*" Again, visualise images corresponding to the reminder phrases.

Address emotional or physical symptom: If you examine your symptoms carefully, you will often notice a connection between emotional and physical symptoms. Illustratively, anxiety or panic frequently manifest as discomfort in the stomach or tightness in the chest. Perhaps you will notice a dry throat or sweaty palms. Similarly, it is often possible to deduce the association between physical symptoms and a root emotional factor. Louise Hay's book *Heal your Body* is an excellent resource for help with this type of investigation. The suggested mind-body connections and the corresponding corrective affirmations are highly useful whilst dealing with physical issues.

You have a choice as to whether you would like to tap for

the emotional or physical issue. Either way, both symptoms are likely to benefit. With the anxiety and panic as described before, you could frame set-ups to say, "Even though I have *this huge anxiety...*" or "Even though *my stomach is tied up in knots...*" or "Even though I have this *stifling pressure in my chest...*" or "Even though *I am in total panic...*" Select whichever aspect you can describe and rate SUDs for more clearly. If you do happen to use Louise Hay's books, the suggested affirmations can be used as set-up affirmations and use a key word from the same as a reminder.

Personal improvement: As stated earlier, I suggest that you first tap to eliminate existing negative traits or *shortfalls* in your own perception. After that, frame positive affirmations. You may also combine these two, by using the choices trio.

- Be realistic in your targets: This is an effective way to aspire towards your targets with belief. For instance, if you are trying to increase your stamina and you use the numbers of push-ups that you can perform with ease as a benchmark, please do not aim for an unreasonable three fold increase. Instead, make gradual increases in your number on a regular basis, and adjust your set-up accordingly. For instance you can use, "I enjoy the ease with which I execute ___ push-ups." Start with a fair number, just a little beyond what you manage comfortably at this point. Then over a period of time, keep making plausible increments in this number.

- Use anchors: Another very useful and effective way to frame personal improvement set-ups and reminders is somewhat similar to 'anchoring' used in NLP. 'Anchoring' is the process by which a particular state or response is deliberately associated with a unique 'anchor' or stimulus, and the same state is invoked by recalling this anchor. For example, by training or conditioning oneself to associate the state of 'peace' with a 'lotus', the very thought or sight of a lotus can be used to invoke peace.

Identify a person who is your role model for a quality that you would like to have in yourself. The more your admiration and liking for this person, the better. Then frame your set-up in a way that you model your own behaviour on this person's expertise. Suppose you consider your colleague, Y, to be a great team leader and would like to emulate him, then tap on, "I choose to be as motivating a team leader as Y."

- Using analogy: If you cannot think of someone appropriate for a particular quality you are aspiring towards, you could still use anchors, by framing the set-up as an analogy. For example, "I intend to be as good at marketing, as Sachin Tendulkar is at batting." The comparison to the skills and success of someone you admire acts as an encouragement for yourself. You will then tend to associate your own efforts with the possibility of equal accomplishment.

Needless to say, your behaviour, actions and efforts need to be aligned with your objectives as well. An exaggerated example to make the point, tapping for a 100 per cent score in your tests cannot show results, unless you also make the efforts to study!

8 | When You are Not Seeing Results

*"Many of life's failures are people who did
not realize how close they were to success
when they gave up."*
— **Thomas Edison**

If you do not experience satisfactory results with the
short-cut method, then try the full basic recipe. Despite this, if
you find that there is no change in your SUD, then one or more
of the following remedial measures may be required:

Water: Did you remember to drink water? EFT will not work
if you are dehydrated.

Try being loud and emphatic with the set-up: This seems to
help focus attention and intention.

Try variations in your set-up: Perhaps you need to be more
specific in stating your problem. Or you need to add some
adjective or a keyword to your set-up. Refer to the guidelines
and experiment with different set-ups.

Try the full basic recipe: The additional points and the
gamut procedure may do the trick.

Have someone else tap on you: Introducing another person's energy and intentions can sometimes make a big difference.

Corrections for Polarity Reversal (PR): A particular form of disruption in your energy circuit can be compared to the effect of inserting batteries the wrong way into a device. Naturally, the circuit does not work and no further progress can be achieved, until the batteries are straightened to the correct polarity alignment. PR is considered to be a major factor in self-sabotage behaviour or 'psychological reversal' and is almost always present in the case of chronic issues or disease. The set-up is meant to correct this PR. It may not be required in all cases, but we include it as measure of caution because if PR exists, then nothing will work until it is corrected.

However, sometimes the PR is so severe or chronic, that extra measures may be required for its correction. Listed below are the additional ways to address PR, starting from the simplest, to the more complicated. Go through the list, one at a time, until you find the one that is effective for you. Please note, that it is entirely possible to be reversed only on some particular issues and not others. So you may find that EFT works on some issues, but in some particular cases, you are unable to make any progress whatsoever. Complete lack of progress is a strong indicator of PR.

When you do not make any progress at all, perform any one of the following three PR corrections as an *additional* step before your EFT routine:

1. **Sore spot:** Form set-up at sore spot instead of at the KC point. The photograph shows the similarly located left and right side sore spots. Feel around in growing

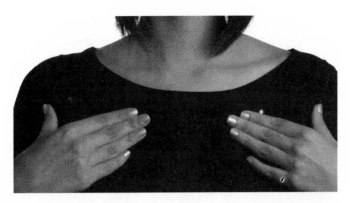

Sore spots

circles in the general area shown in the photograph. You will locate a tender spot that feels sore or painful on rubbing. These two mirror points are points of lymphatic congestion. Rubbing them dispenses this congestion. Some people have a little difficulty in locating their sore spots, or find them to be too painful and hence we first try the set-up at the KC point. However, if that does not work, then repeat your set-up statement three times, while rubbing your left sore spot, or both your sore spots simultaneously.

2. **Belly button correction:** Dr Barbara L. Mallory has given her kind consent for sharing her simple and effective PR correction technique in this book.

Take a deep breath and release. Mentally focus on the issue you are having difficulty with. Then refer to the photographs and do the following:

a. Press the fingers of one hand firmly on your navel and keep them there.

b. Rub under your nose with the index finger of the other hand for six to eight seconds.

2b, Belly button correction

2c, Belly button correction

2d, Belly button correction

2e, Belly button correction

c.   Rub under your lower lip for six to eight seconds.

d.   Extend fingers and thumb to massage both collarbone points for six to eight seconds.

e.   Massage your tailbone for six to eight seconds.

f.   Reverse hands and repeat the procedure (optional, but recommended).

3. **Collarbone breathing:** This correction takes a little longer time and is more complicated than the belly button correction. Take a deep breath and release. Mentally focus on the issue you are having difficulty with. Then do the following:

A. Touch your right collarbone point with your right index and middle finger tips, keeping rest of the hand and elbow away from the body. Now tap the gamut point of your right hand continuously with your left hand index and middle finger tips. While tapping, do the following five breathing exercises:

a.   Breathe half way in and hold it for seven taps.

b.   Breathe all the way in and hold it for seven taps.

c.   Breathe half way out and hold it for seven taps.

d.   Breathe all the way out and hold it for seven taps.

e.   Breathe normally for seven taps.

B. Now move your right hand to the left collarbone point and repeat the above procedure.

C. Bend your right hand into a fist and place the second joints of index and middle fingers on the right

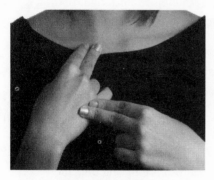

3A, Collarbone breathing

3B, Collarbone breathing

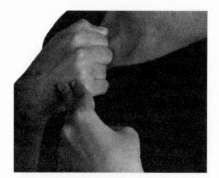

3C, Collarbone breathing

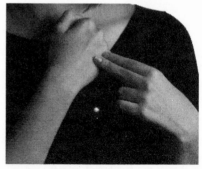

3D, Collarbone breathing

collarbone point. Repeat the five breathing exercises while tapping on the gamut point with left hand.

D. Move your hand in the same position to the left collarbone point and repeat the five breathing exercises while tapping on the gamut point with left hand.

Now repeat steps A, B, C and D, using the fingertips and joints of the left hand on the collarbone points while tapping the gamut point with the right hand.

Energy toxins: We are constantly exposed to a large number of chemicals, pollutants, etc. Just as we may develop allergic reactions to substances, certain things may act as irritants or cause disturbances to our energy system. These may be present in our food, clothing, environment, medicines, etc. There may also be electromagnetic or geopathic factors involved. While you may or may not show physical reactions, such as rashes or breathing difficulties, as are often seen with allergens, these energy toxins may yet be interfering with your energy system.

The simplest remedial measure you can attempt is to try EFT at a different location, at different times, on different days. You may be able to notice when it doesn't seem to work and pinpoint the *energy toxin.*

However, it may take more persistent efforts to locate the culprits.

If you have any form of implants in your body, such as metal fillings, pins, rods, etc. these should be considered as possible allergens or energy toxins. Yeast and calcium sensitivities are also fairly common, especially in women. Any known allergens are also possibilities.

Next, you could try eliminating suspected food articles, perfumes, detergents, etc. one at a time, and observe any changes. You could start with some of the more common allergens such as wheat, peanuts, sugar, alcohol, nicotine and coffee.

There are two more systematic ways of identifying your possible energy toxins. One is muscle testing and the other is dowsing (using a pendulum). Describing the use of both is beyond the scope of this book, and you would need to find an expert to help you out. However, it could save you a great deal of time.

Whether by observation, elimination, muscle testing or dowsing, once you have discovered your energy toxins, you can either try to eliminate or avoid them, or use EFT to address this problem first. Refer to the section on 'EFT for substance sensitivities' on how to use EFT for such substances. Strangely, EFT seems to work when tapping for the substance sensitivity, and once that is cleared, your original issue can be addressed as well.

Energy toxins and allergens have a strong tendency to return and you should routinely monitor to ensure that the problem remains cleared, for one or two months. The energy system needs to be *retrained* to stay corrected. But after some time, the system is likely to settle down.

Secondary benefits syndrome: Secondary benefits refers to the gains of continuing to have the issue in your life. For example, a sick person gets more attention from family members, or the *high* from alcohol or cigarettes numbs you towards a negative emotion or situation. The person may or may not be consciously choosing to have this secondary benefit. It is entirely possible that he does not even realise it. Even after it is identified, there may be reluctance or complete denial. Hence these issues are better handled by working with someone else or with a professional.

If you would like to attempt EFT yourself, suggested set-ups would be of the form:

- Even though I may be having this ___, because of ____ benefit, I now choose to let go of this problem.

- Even though I need ____, to feel (happy/safe/etc.), I deeply...

- Even though I don't want to let go of _____, I deeply and completely...

- Even though I refuse to give (*this issue*) up, I deeply and completely...

- Even though I deserve ____, I now give myself permission to heal.

Internet: Search EFT sites for cases similar to yours and try set-ups that worked for them. There are hundreds of success stories available online. You can even contact practitioners and forums for help with your queries. You will be amazed at how much help is available and that too for free.

Consult a practitioner: A lot of progress can be made by the newcomer working on his own. But a professional is bound to have more experience and expertise, besides being an objective third party, who can recognise underlying issues and patterns far more easily. Relatively, the average cost of a consultation is fairly reasonable. Consider seeing a professional for your chronic, complex and challenging problems.

9 | SCORE with EFT

"What we are today comes from our thoughts of yesterday, and our present thoughts build our life of tomorrow: Our life is the creation of our mind."

— **Buddha**

Each of us is blessed with talents and great potential. But our own thoughts, beliefs, experiences, emotional baggage and patterns can stifle us into being less than what we are capable of being. If you are determined to set yourself free from all such restrictions and are eager to actualise your true potential, then SCORE can help you transform yourself from who you are, into who you want to be.

Though it may appear complex at first glance, this systematic way of eliminating your limitations and enhancing your positive features can be implemented with ease and little effort.

You will require an initial time investment of about 100 minutes, followed by a daily investment of *only* ten minutes. Decide a time cycle for this exercise and review the charts at the end of the period. Twenty-one days would be a good time frame. It allows sufficient time for major changes to take place and yet, is not too long a gap between reviews. If you prefer, you can opt for a longer cycle of say ninety or 120 days. But as EFT results are faster than more common ways of personal development, a shorter duration may be more appropriate.

The five steps of SCORE are as follows:

S   Do a SWOT analysis for your self.

C   Construct corresponding EFT set-ups as per the personal SWOT analysis.

O   One full round of tapping for each of your strengths and opportunities.

R   Routine ten minute tapping on a daily basis.

E   Evaluate progress and make necessary changes at the end of twenty-one days.

Step one: Management students and professionals may be well familiar with the use of SWOT analysis in business. This same system of identifying Strengths, Weaknesses, Opportunities and Threats can be productively used for radical personal transformation.

For the purpose of our exercise, we need a grid that is somewhat different from the traditional 2x2 SWOT grid. This is the grid that you will need to fill out:

Personal SWOT analysis

	Physical	Emotional	Trait	Financial
Strengths				
Weaknesses				
Opportunities				
Threats				

Instructions on how to fill the grid:

Place only one item in each cell in this table. Do not spend more than two or three minutes on each cell. The first few items/issues that pop into your head are likely to be the ones you feel most strongly about. Use one or two keywords that are representative of the selected item and describe the item exactly the way you see things. Whenever possible, be specific and concise. We will be using these to frame your set-ups in the next step.

Questions and examples to help you locate your own corresponding items are given below:

Strengths: Identify items that you consider to be your *existing* strengths or assets.

Physical

Are you in sound health? Do you like the way you look? Do you have great stamina? Is your hearing particularly sharp? Are you proud of being able to run a marathon? Cell examples: 'perfect health', 'attractive', 'great figure', 'beautiful eyes', 'fit as a horse', etc.

Emotional

Are you happy, enthusiastic, light-hearted, loving, forgiving, generous, compassionate, cooperative, patient, tolerant or empathetic? Pick any quality that makes you feel good about the way you emote and interact with others. Cell examples: 'enjoy life', 'spread cheer', 'generous', 'patient', etc.

Trait

Which qualities do you like or admire most about yourself? Cell examples: 'determination', 'resilience', 'loyalty', 'honesty', 'discipline', 'intellect', 'innovative','logic', 'pragmatism', etc.

Financial

Are you happy with your bank balance, your salary, or your second car? What makes you feel grateful and abundant? Is it your self-owned house or the latest cellphone? The item need not be highly valuable, but should invoke a sense of gratitude and satisfaction. At the very least, remember to be grateful for your ability to meet your basic requirements. Cell examples: 'recent increment', 'new watch', 'booming stock investments', 'own house', 'monthly savings scheme', 'recent gift', etc.

Weaknesses: Identify items that you consider to be the *existing* limitations and would like to reduce or eliminate from your life.

Physical

Do you suffer from any disease or discomfort? Are you overweight? Do you have any nagging aches or pains? Cell examples: 'weakling', 'anorexic', 'migraines', 'poor stamina', '__ allergy', 'usually feel exhausted', etc.

Emotional

Are there any negative emotions that constantly plague you? Is there any emotional characteristic that you would rather not have? Cell examples: 'unenthusiastic', 'withdrawn', 'bored', 'depressed', 'constantly anxious', 'short-tempered', 'excessively possessive', 'immature', 'defensive', 'unresponsive', etc.

Trait

What do you consider to be lacking in your personality? What holds you back and limits you from actualising your full potential? What criticisms have you received from others? Cell examples: 'overly critical', 'aggressive', 'never on time', 'indecisive', 'spineless', 'lack focus', 'procrastinate', etc.

Financial

Are there any limiting beliefs about money? What mistakes do you commonly make in your money matters? Which is the poor saving or spending habit that you have? If you can't think of anything, you may use 'could manage my money better' as there is always room for improvement! Cell examples: 'can never afford ___', 'will never get that raise', 'never that lucky', 'believe good guys finish last'; 'spendthrift', 'always in debt', 'overdue credit cards', 'no savings', 'don't plan for future', etc.

Opportunities: Include elements that you would like to incorporate into your life. These may include strengths you are looking for or enhancement of your present strengths. List these in the positive form.

Physical

Would you like to be more healthy or energetic? Would you like to swim more laps? Would you prefer healthier eating habits? Are you working to build a six-pack or to trim your waistline? Cell examples: 'more stamina', 'trim waist', 'eighteen inch biceps', 'healthy diet', etc.

Emotional

Is there a better way for you to interact with others? Is there another way you would like to cope with your emotions? Cell examples: 'better listener', 'patient', 'calm', 'peaceful', 'loving', 'trusting', etc.

Trait

Which qualities would enhance your performance and personality? Which attribute needs further work? Cell examples: 'dependable', 'determined', 'goal oriented', 'confident', 'versatile', 'adaptable', 'optimistic', 'self-starter', 'public speaking skills', etc.

Financial

What money management skills do you need to learn or adopt? How can you improve your financial position? Cell examples: 'educate myself further', 'listen to my advisor', 'understand interest rates', 'keep up with news', 'maintain timely records', 'monitor portfolio', etc.

Threats: Include habits and qualities that need to be checked, especially those with the potential to spiral into major problem areas.

Physical

Do you disregard your health? Which habits are detrimental to your well-being? Cell examples: 'lack exercise routine', 'sleep poorly', 'eat junk food', 'binge on weekends', 'neglect (health issue)', 'overeat sweets', 'starve myself', 'smoke', etc.

Emotional

Which feelings and sentiments would you like to check? Any habitual reactions or behaviour patterns that you would like to release? Cell examples: 'lethargic', 'overly laid-back', 'lazy', 'dependent on others', 'cannot do without food/drugs/alcohol/cigarettes', 'violent temper', 'afraid of ___', 'constantly worry over ___', 'easily bored', etc.

Trait

Which aspects of your personality would you like to discard or transform? Are there any qualities that are limiting you from being your best? Cell examples: 'habitually lie', 'avoid responsibility', 'lack willpower', 'make ill-thought decisions', 'feel uncomfortable in the limelight', 'poor communicator', etc.

Financial

Are you being careless with your finances? Do you have any potentially expensive habits spinning out of your control? Cell examples: 'spend impulsively', 'spend irresponsibly', 'rotate credit', 'enjoy gambling', 'don't want to bother about the future', 'neglect post-retirement planning', 'must go bar-hopping everyday', etc.

Step two: Construct set-ups corresponding to the personal SWOT table and fill in the table given here.

SWOT set-ups table

	Physical	Emotional	Trait	Financial
Strengths	1.	7.	13.	19.
Weaknesses Negative Component	2.	8.	14.	20.
Positive Component	3.	9.	15.	21.
Opportunities	4.	10.	16.	22.
Threats Negative Component	5.	11.	17.	23.
Positive Component	6.	12.	18.	24.

Use the tips given for your convenience. If you still encounter any difficulty, please refer to 'General Guidelines for Framing Set-ups and Reminder phrases', or the various examples given in the book.

Tips for Strengths set-ups:

Use phrases similar to one of the following, with corresponding cell item from the Strengths in personal SWOT analysis table.

- I appreciate ___
- I am grateful for ___
- I admire ___ about myself
- I love ___ about myself
- I am proud of ___
- I enjoy ___

For instance, if you have written 'good health' as your Physical Strength in the personal SWOT analysis table, then write, "I am grateful for my good health" under Strengths-Physical (cell number one), in the SWOT set-ups table.

Tips for Weaknesses, Negative Component

Write 'Even though I am _____' and fill in the blank with corresponding cell item from the Weaknesses in personal SWOT analysis table. Do not write any positive component (like 'deeply and completely accept myself') here.

For instance, if you have written 'shy' under Weaknesses-Emotional in the personal SWOT analysis table, then write, 'Even though I am usually shy' in Weaknesses-Negative Component-Emotional (cell number eight).

Tips for Weaknesses, Positive Component

Identify the positive and *opposite* state of whatever was written in the corresponding Weaknesses cell in the personal SWOT analysis table. Use this with a phrase similar to one of the following:

- I intend to be ___
- I would rather be ___
- I choose to ____ now
- I prefer _____ now

E.g. if you have written 'shy' under Weaknesses-Emotional, then a positive and opposite state is 'outgoing'. So your statement would be, 'I choose to be outgoing now' under Weaknesses-Positive Component-Emotional (cell number nine).

Tips for Opportunities set-ups:

Use phrases similar to one of the following, with corresponding cell item from the personal SWOT analysis table.

- I choose to ___
- I intend to ____
- I am now ____
- I am learning ___
- I grow more ____ each day
- I get better at ___ every day

E.g. if you have written 'public speaking skills' as your Trait Opportunity in the personal SWOT analysis, then write 'I get better at public speaking every day' or 'I am now a great orator' under Opportunities-Trait (cell number sixteen), in the SWOT set-ups table.

Tips for Threats, Negative Component:

Write, 'Even though I _____' and fill in the blank with corresponding cell item from the Threats in personal SWOT analysis. Do not write any positive component (like 'deeply and completely accept myself') here.

E.g. if you have written 'spend carelessly' under Threats-Financial in the personal SWOT analysis, then write 'Even though I spend carelessly' in Threats-Negative Component-Financial (cell number twenty-three).

Tips for Threats, Positive Component:

Identify the positive and *opposite* state of whatever was written in the corresponding Threats cell in the personal SWOT analysis table. Use this with a phrase similar to one of the following:

- I choose to ____ now
- I intend to be ___
- I would rather be ___
- I prefer _____ now
- I adopt ___

E.g. if you had written 'spend carelessly' under Threats-Financial, then a positive and opposite state is 'careful spender' or 'thrifty'. So write 'I choose to be a careful spender now' or 'I would rather be thrifty now' under Threats-Positive Component-Financial (cell number twenty-four).

You have now completed the more time consuming part

of this exercise. Completing your SWOT and deciding upon what you would like instead, is what requires some effort. EFT now makes the implementation of this plan relatively simple and automatic.

Step three: One round of EFT is to be performed on *each* of the set-ups in the Strengths and Opportunities rows from the SWOT set-ups table. Hence, you are required to do eight full rounds of EFT, one each, for the set-ups listed in cells one, seven, thirteen, nineteen, four, ten, sixteen and twenty-two. I recommend using the full basic recipe (though you may use the short-cut method) as you will be tapping full rounds on these affirmations only this once. Use the entire sentence as your reminder phrase. These eight rounds should take you about twelve to fifteen minutes. This is an attempt to consolidate your positive attributes here. They will be reinforced on a daily basis.

You have completed the exercise for day one.

Step four: Routine daily tapping of ten minutes for the balance twenty days. Each day, set aside ten minutes for this exercise. Ideally, do it first thing in the morning, or last thing in the night. If you wish to repeat this ten minute exercise more than once a day, that is also perfectly fine.

a. Use the first eight minutes to work on *any one* of the Weaknesses or Threats items. Rotate the selection, so that over a period of time, all the eight items receive attention at some time. If your SUD drops to zero within a few minutes, and you have time left, you can start work on another of these eight items the same day. However, work on only one or two items a day, as you should attempt to bring the SUD as low as possible. The obvious option would be the choices trio method, using the Negative and Positive components of the affirmation. You may use the short-cut method, but switch to the full basic recipe, if you are making slow progress with the SUDs.

Continuing our earlier example, the full set-up for the Emotional Weakness would be, Cell eight + Cell nine — 'Even though *I am usually shy*, I choose to be outgoing now'. Reminder phrase would be the keyword from the negative component (and the full positive phrase for the positive round, in the choices trio).

Hence, your total eight set-ups are given by:

- Cell two + Cell three
- Cell eight + Cell nine
- Cell fourteen + Cell fifteen
- Cell twenty + Cell twenty-one
- Cell five + Cell six
- Cell eleven + Cell twelve
- Cell seventeen + Cell eighteen
- Cell twenty-three + Cell twenty-four

Consequently, these daily eight minutes are utilised for removing or reducing your undesirables.

b. The daily reinforcement of existing and desired positives will contribute significantly to your transformation. The makeover round will take only two minutes, you are encouraged to repeat it as often as you like during the day. You may want to record your own voice reading or singing out the set-up affirmations, on your cell phone or music player, so that you can listen and tap along effortlessly.

Use the text from the corresponding cells in the SWOT set-ups table and tap five to seven times at indicated point, as per the following:

Point	Affirmation
KC:	Every day, in every way, I am getting better and better.
KC:	Every day, in every way, I am getting better and better.
KC:	Every day, in every way, I am getting better and better.
EB:	Cell one
SE:	Cell three
UE:	Cell four
UN:	Cell six
CH:	Cell seven
CB:	Cell nine
UA:	Cell ten
CRH:	Cell twelve
KC:	Every day, in every way, I am getting better and better.
KC:	Every day, in every way, I am getting better and better.
KC:	Every day, in every way, I am getting better and better.
EB:	Cell thirteen

SE:	Cell fifteen
UE:	Cell sixteen
UN:	Cell eighteen
CH:	Cell nineteen
CB:	Cell twenty-one
UA:	Cell twenty-two
CRH:	Cell twenty-four

Step five: Evaluate your progress at the end of twenty-one days. Sit down with your personal SWOT analysis and reassess all the items. Where the SUDS are down to zero, you may drop that Weakness or Threat item and replace it with a fresh one. Any item that continues to be a challenge should be retained. If you are satisfied that the Strengths and Opportunities have been sufficiently imbibed, you may replace them with newer improvements that you would like to adopt.

This cyclical process of appraisal, remedial tapping and reassessment is a methodical and effective way of implementing continuous personal improvement, in all areas of your life.

SCORE Illustration

S, Step 1: Personal SWOT analysis

	Physical	Emotional	Trait	Financial
Strengths	Remarkable stamina	Highly compassion-ate	Pay attention to details	Medical insurance
Weaknesses	Get migraines	Emotionally vulnerable	Procrast-inate	Must struggle to make ends meet

Opportunities	Start gyming regularly	More self-assured	More creative	Learn to understand balance sheets
Threats	Eat at irregular hours	Sensitive to criticism	Lack resilience	Spend impulsively

C, Step 2: Construct SWOT set-ups

	Physical	Emotional	Trait	Financial
Strengths	1. I am grateful for my remarkable stamina	7. I love that I am highly compassion-ate	13. I am proud of my ability for detailed work	19. I am grateful to afford medical insurance
Weaknesses Negative Component	2. Even though I get migraines	8. Even though I feel emotionally vulnerable	14. Even though I tend to procrast-inate	20. Even though I believe I must struggle to make ends meet
Positive Component	3. I intend to enjoy perfect health and well-being now	9. I prefer to be emotionally strong now	15. I now intend to meet deadlines with ease	21. I would rather be financially comfort-able now
Opportunities	4. I choose to gym regularly	10. I grow more self-assured everyday	16. I choose to be more creative	22. I am learning to understand balance sheets
Threats Negative Component	5. Even though I eat at irregular hours	11. Even though I am sensitive to criticism	17. Even though I lack resilience	23. Even though I tend to spend impulsively

Contd

Positive Component	6. I intend to eat at proper meal times now	12. I choose to adopt positive suggestions now	18. I now adopt a never-say-die attitude	24. I prefer to spend prudently now

O, Step 3: One round of EFT each for:

- Cell one   I am grateful for my remarkable stamina.

- Cell seven   I love that I am highly compassionate.

- Cell thirteen   I am proud of my ability for detailed work.

- Cell nineteen   I am grateful to afford medical insurance.

- Cell four   I choose to gym regularly.

- Cell ten   I grow more self-assured everyday.

- Cell sixteen   I choose to be more creative.

- Cell twenty-two   I am learning to understand balance sheets.

R, Step 4a: Routine tap on *any one or two* of the following everyday. See detailed guidelines.

- Cell two + Cell three
  Even though I *get migraines*, I intend to enjoy perfect health and well-being now.

- Cell eight + Cell nine
  Even though I *feel emotionally vulnerable*, I prefer to be emotionally strong now.

- Cell fourteen + Cell fifteen
  Even though I *tend to procrastinate*, I now intend to meet deadlines with ease.

- Cell twenty + Cell twenty-one
  Even though *I believe I must struggle to make ends meet*, I would rather be financially comfortable now.

- Cell five + Cell six
  Even though I *eat at irregular hours*, I intend to eat at proper meal times now.

- Cell eleven + Cell twelve
  Even though I am *sensitive to criticism*, I choose to adopt positive suggestions now.

- Cell seventeen + Cell eighteen
  Even though I *lack resilience*, I now adopt a never-say-die attitude.

- Cell twenty-three + Cell twenty-four
  Even though I *tend to spend impulsively*, I prefer to spend prudently now.

R, Step 4b: Routine tap the makeover daily.

KC:	Every day, in every way, I am getting better and better.
KC:	Every day, in every way, I am getting better and better.
KC:	Every day, in every way, I am getting better and better.
EB:	(Cell one) I am grateful for my remarkable stamina.
SE:	(Cell three) I intend to enjoy perfect health and well-being now.

UE: (Cell four) I choose to gym regularly.

UN: (Cell six) I intend to eat at proper meal times now.

CH: (Cell seven) I love that I am highly compassionate.

CB: (Cell nine) I prefer to be emotionally strong now.

UA: (Cell ten) I grow more self-assured everyday.

CRH: (Cell twelve) I choose to adopt positive suggestions now.

KC: Every day, in every way, I am getting better and better.

KC: Every day, in every way, I am getting better and better.

KC: Every day, in every way, I am getting better and better.

EB: (Cell thirteen) I am proud of my ability for detailed work.

SE: (Cell fifteen) I now intend to meet deadlines with ease.

UE: (Cell sixteen) I choose to be more creative.

UN: (Cell eighteen) I now adopt a never-say-die attitude.

CH: (Cell nineteen) I am grateful to afford medical insurance.

CB: (Cell twenty-one) I would rather be financially comfortable now.

UA: (Cell twenty-two) I am learning to understand balance sheets.

CRH: (Cell twenty-four) I prefer to spend prudently now.

E, Step 5: Evaluate after twenty-one days and start afresh.

SCORE tables templates

(Photocopies can be used for each evaluation).

Personal SWOT analysis

	Physical	Emotional	Trait	Financial
Strengths				
Weaknesses				
Opportunities				
Threats				

SWOT set-ups

	Physical	Emotional	Trait	Financial
Strengths	1.	7.	13.	19.
Weaknesses Negative Component	2.	8.	14.	20.
Positive Component	3.	9.	15.	21.

Contd

Opportunities	4.	10.	16.	22.
Threats Negative Component	5.	11.	17.	23.
Positive Component	6.	12.	18.	24.

10 | Proxy or Surrogate Tapping

*"The only work that will ultimately bring
any good to any of us is the work of
contributing to the healing of the world."*
— **Marianne Williamson**

EFT works by addressing energy disruptions or blockages. Because of this, it is possible to send healing over geographical distances. While this idea may seem somewhat strange or surprising to newcomers, energy practitioners are well versed with the concept of distance healing. Illustratively, advanced reiki practitioners send reiki to recipients at other locations, on a routine basis.

Spiritual teachings propose that we are all manifestations of the same singularity. Hence, we are all connected and distance healing is a natural corollary to such beliefs.

If such ideas and discussions are beyond your present comfort zone, consider routine matters that surround us on a daily basis. Remember that you are being bombarded by any number of energies that are going unnoticed by your physical senses. Electronic devices and medical diagnostic tools such as X-ray and ultrasound machines, radio, television, mobiles, etc. are constantly sending and receiving huge amounts of energy and information all the time. But we are unable to perceive these without appropriate devices to capture and convert this energy into forms that we can see or hear. However, this does not mean that they do not exist or do not have their consequences.

Just as you were invited to try out the exercises in 'Getting Started', to convince yourself as to whether EFT works or not, I would suggest that you conduct trials of proxy or surrogate tapping, so that you can decide for yourself.

By proxy or surrogate tapping, we refer to the use of EFT by one person on behalf of another. Your tapping on your own self, with the intention of healing another is proxy tapping.

10.1: When to use proxy or surrogate tapping

Sometimes the person requiring healing or assistance may not be in a position to do the tapping for himself. He may be too unwell, or disturbed, or perhaps requires urgent assistance, and there is insufficient time or opportunity to teach EFT for his own use. Proxy tapping can hence be useful for the disabled, elderly, infants or young children and also animals and pets.

On occasion, the person may be tapping himself, but is dealing with highly challenging issues. At such times, your proxy tapping acts as an additional support and input.

In all cases, wherever possible, I recommend that the recipient be encouraged to learn and practise EFT for himself.

It is fascinating to see how well animals respond to EFT. Also, on many occasions, I have seen the dog, horse or bird turn and look directly at you, as though acknowledging your tapping.

10.2: Are there any limitations on the use of proxy tapping?

Proxy tapping may be compared to praying for another's welfare. The intention is to help and support another person in his situation. Importantly, one should remember that in spite of the best of intentions, making choices on behalf of another is inappropriate and against the paradigm of free will. Your views and desires may or may not be in agreement with that of the recipient. And no matter how unsuitable you may think their choices to be, you cannot live their life for them.

10.3: So how do we solve this quandary?

Firstly, before beginning any form of distance healing, state the intention that, "This healing is intended in the highest good of (recipient)."

Secondly, do not make choices that are not yours to make! Use your common sense and exercise reasonable judgment. An extreme illustration that I frequently quote is the query I received from a young teenager. She asked me if tapping for, "Even though X doesn't love me, I choose to have him fall in love with me" would work! I told her that this was completely against basic principles and ethics, and further, I really doubt if it would work. Similarly, please do not consider trying EFT for negative intentions such as "X should not get the promotion". If you want a better position, tap for your own improvement and success.

10.4: Do I need the recipient's permission for proxy tapping?

No prior permission is necessary for proxy EFT to work.

Having said that, do keep in mind the discussion in the earlier paragraph.

Some people feel uncomfortable tapping without permission, and you are encouraged to follow your own conscience in the matter. If you are confused about the ethics, consider these pertinent questions: Do we ever pause to take permission from a person before we say unpleasant things about him? Do you hesitate in praying for someone or sending good wishes their way? Do you take permission to do something loving and healing for a dear one?

10.5: How does one do proxy tapping?

There are two ways to do proxy tapping:

1. First state, "I am __ for the purpose of this intended healing", naming the intended recipient. For instance, if you are tapping for the benefit of Arjun say, "I am Arjun for the purpose of this intended healing". After this, you continue with selected EFT rounds in exactly the same way as when you would have tapped for yourself. To clarify, you tap on your own body.

   Personally, I do not recommend this method, though it is widely practised.

2. The second method of proxy tapping is simple and effective. We only modify the set-up statements to reflect the recipient's name and issue. Hence the relevant default set-up becomes:

   "Even though *Arjun has_____*, I deeply and completely love, forgive and accept *him*."

   Again, the EFT rounds are performed in exactly the same fashion as you would for yourself, tapping on your own body.

I prefer this second method, as it is very analogous to performing EFT on an as is where is basis. You are describing the situation as you see it and expressing loving support for the concerned individual. Very few ethical questions can arise under such circumstances.

You may also frame other set-ups, bearing in mind the limitations discussed earlier. Examples:

- Even though *Arjun is breathless(or asthmatic)*, he can breathe fully and easily now.

- Even though *Arjun has difficulty sitting still*, he can be calm and attentive now.

- Even though *Arjun is alone and terrified*, he can feel safe now.

- Even though *Arjun feels completely hopeless*, he can find his way out of this situation.

I like using the word *can* as much as possible, in proxy set-ups. I consider it to be comparable to opening doors or creating possible options for the recipient. Coupled with the *highest good* intention, I believe this to be one of the least interfering, yet most supportive ways to provide healing opportunity to the recipient.

You may use any one of the three methods for the EFT rounds — one of short-cut, basic recipe or choices trio for proxy tapping.

11 | Specific Areas of Application with Sample Set-ups

"Most of your reactions are echoes from the past. You do not really live in the present."
— **Gaelic Proverb**

11.1: EFT for substance sensitivities

Sameera came to me with symptoms of chronic fatigue, body ache and listlessness. All medical tests had diagnosed her as normal and she was at a loss as to how to proceed. In my experience, such cases often have substance sensitivities. Using dowsing, I tested her for the most common sensitivities and found that she was sensitive to calcium and yeast. We did five short-cut rounds for each sensitivity, using, "Even though I have a problem with calcium, I choose to have a healthy relationship with calcium now" and "Even though I have a problem with yeast, I choose to be healthy now." Dowsing indicated that the sensitivity was cleared. I asked her to continue tapping one round each, everyday for fifteen days, to prevent its recurrence.

Within two days she reported improved energy and lesser pain. Over a period of about one month, she continued to improve steadily. Sameera now has stray incidences of fatigue and body ache. She is far more active and enthusiastic than before and continues to use EFT as and when required.

In this case, tapping directly for the sensitivity was sufficient. However, sometimes, unravelling and addressing emotional contributors also becomes necessary.

Substance sensitivity refers to reactions to allergens, or allergies as they are commonly known, as well as reactions to certain substances or energy toxins, as described in 'When You are Not Seeing Results'.

As discussed in the said chapter, there are various ways to try and identify a substance you are sensitive to. Once you have identified it, EFT can be used to treat this sensitivity.

Please note that allergic reactions may at times be serious or even life-threatening. Hence you are advised to take all possible precautions and to test yourself under medical supervision, before assuming that the allergy has been completely resolved.

An important note: Typically, 'allergies' are associated with sudden, intense and physical symptoms such as itching, breathing difficulty, etc. In fact, substance sensitivity may manifest in more subtle ways. It may contribute towards depression, anxiety, panic attacks, migraines, weight gain and many other such symptoms that are not commonly associated with an allergy or sensitivity.

Another surprising piece of information: If you have cravings for a particular substance, it is highly possible that you have an allergy or sensitivity towards it. Medicines and surgical implants are also common problem areas.

If you are not making satisfactory or consistent progress with EFT, it is very likely that you have some substance sensitivity.

There is a proposition that sensitivities are in fact the body's inappropriate, but conditioned response to a trauma. The body associates the substance with a trauma and consequently responds aggressively to the substance, when it is presented again. During tapping, sensitivity is sometimes traced back to a strong emotional reaction to an adverse situation.

A hypothetical case can illustrate the logic. John has a severe allergy to cheese and eggs. On questioning, he reveals that the allergy started around the time he got divorced. Further questions and tapping (EFT) may reveal that he often had fights at the breakfast table. Subconsciously, he has come to associate his breakfast food with negative emotions and situations, and his body presents strong reactions whenever confronted with this "reminder" or trigger food.

EFT and other holistic practitioners address the symptoms (allergy and/or depression) as well as the emotional reaction to the original episode.

The offending substance may be an ingestant (food, drink, vitamin, medicine, etc.), an inhalant (perfume, cleaning agent, etc.), injectant (drugs, medicines) or a contactant (fabric, metal, etc.). Interestingly, if we are sensitive to a vitamin or food, we do not absorb it properly. Hence you may be showing a vitamin deficiency for a vitamin you are sensitive to. Geopathic sensitivity to a particular location or sensitivity to elements such as wood, metal or water is also possible.

Smells often play a particularly important role in sensitivities. The only sensory input that goes directly to the amygdala is that of smell. Hence smells can have a powerful influence in triggering our feelings and emotions.

Once you have identified the substance, you may address the sensitivity directly with four to five rounds of tapping, using: "Even though I have a problem with_____I deeply and completely love, forgive and accept myself."

Use *still have this problem* for subsequent rounds. Most of the time, four to five rounds of even the short-cut method can clear the problem. If you are not making progress, refer to 'When You are Not Seeing Results'. A professional would use muscle testing or dowsing to verify the change. If you do not have any dangerous reactions to the substance, you can try exposing yourself to it and see if more rounds are needed. However, for serious reactions, please visit an allergy testing centre, before exposing yourself to the substance.

If you have been able to identify any troubling or traumatic memories with the substance in question, then tap for all aspects of that event as well.

Caution: Naturally, the body will not stop reacting to substances that are toxic for it, for example, cigarette smoke. However, tapping for the sensitivity can help boost immunity and tolerance for unavoidable exposure.

11.2: EFT for children

> "We need to teach the next generation of children from Day One that they are responsible for their lives. Mankind's greatest gift, also its greatest curse, is that we have free choice. We can make our choices built from love or from fear."
>
> — **Elisabeth Kubler-Ross**

Sachin, a five-year-old had developed a tendency for nightmares. Despite being accustomed to sleeping alone from early age, he became reluctant to sleep alone as he had nightly terrors of *thieves* breaking into their house. Sachin was scared every night and woke up crying and shouting aloud.

However, one day he remembered that he had seen his mother using EFT and was quite fascinated by the gamut humming. She had explained that she was using it to address something she was upset about.

So he came up with the idea to ask his mother to tap on him in the night at bedtime! His mother would tuck him into bed and then tap on him, using the set-up: "Even though Sachin used to have 'thieves dreams', he now has fun dreams about the Pooh bear instead." (Sachin was very fond of Winnie the Pooh). Sachin began sleeping soundly again, waking up fresh and happy without experiencing any nightmares. After about a week, he was to go to his grandparents for vacation, so he ensured that his mother taught his grandmother the same routine for his benefit! Gradually, after a few days, the need for EFT also fell away. The nightmares have not recurred.

For infants and younger children, you may consider using proxy tapping. You may also say the set-ups and reminder phrase, while tapping gently on their body. If they are too restless, do this while they are sleeping.

However, children generally love EFT and are happy to try it out for themselves. They have neither inhibitions, nor expectations and usually consider the whole process to be a fun filled game that leaves them feeling better and more positive.

They love tapping with both hands, and doing the Under the Arm, UA point in 'monkey fashion' (tap right side with right hand and simultaneously, the left side with left hand) almost unfailingly brings up a round of giggles.

The easiest way to get them to tap is to describe what you are teaching as a game similar to 'Simon Says', where they are required to follow your words and movements. Using a 'tappy bear', stuffed toy or doll to demonstrate the tapping procedure has also proven popular. You can also give them this doll to tap, when they are upset. It allows them to vent their feelings as though they were sharing them with a friend.

With particularly disruptive or angry kids, simply tapping on the KC and index and little finger points, while continuing a normal dialogue, can be very helpful in calming them. If possible, have them do the same.

Children seem to take up more intuitively to EFT and they often come up with diverse ways in which to use it. Do not worry a great deal over framing their set-ups and reminder phrases. They are already well tuned in to whatever is occupying their attention. So the tapping alone is often very beneficial.

Instead of asking them to fix a number for SUDs, have them indicate 'how upset' they are by stretching out their arms. Tell them that wide apart arms indicate very upset and palms close together mean the problem is gone. This is an uncomplicated way for them to convey 'how upset' they are.

The default set-up that many EFT practitioners use for kids is: "Even though I (*am upset/sad/afraid*), I am a great kid!" or "I (*am upset/sad/afraid*) *and* I am a great kid!"

You will be amazed to see how much the children enjoy saying this aloud.

Learning disorders: There are innumerable ways in which

EFT can help a child. Unfortunately, the scope of this book is limited to introduce the basics. Nevertheless, I would like to mention that EFT has demonstrated notable success in learning disorders. Naturally, this is a complex area that would entail a great deal of discussion.

EFT can be used to address the specific symptoms of dyslexia, dyscalculia, and other disorders as also the associated affective responses like feelings of discouragement, anger, confusion, despair, etc.

Some sample set-ups to address dyslexia:

- Even though the *letters are dancing*, I am a great kid.
- Even though the *letters are swimming around*, I am ok.
- Even though *I feel stupid*, I accept myself.
- Even though *I can't get the words right*, I am a wonderful kid.
- I hate school because *I can't read the blackboard*, but I love myself anyway.
- Even though the *kids laugh at me*, I accept myself.
- I am *scared of teacher* but I am a brave kid who enjoys school anyway.

EFT for juniors: Daily tapping on positive statements has a wonderful and liberating effect on children. The following simplified EFT routine intends to remove all the common fears and blocks that many of the children face in our present schooling systems. Can you imagine the effect of children tapping these positive statements daily, in their assembly sessions? I urge anyone with the access to school authorities to try and have this incorporated in as many school routines as is possible!

I love myself, my family,	Karate Chop (KC, left)
my friends, and teachers too!	Karate Chop (KC, right)
School is fun and easy,	Eyebrow (EB), both together
every day I learn something new!	Side of the Eye (SE), both together
I like working with numbers,	Under the Eye (UE), both together
painting and singing too!	Under the Nose (UN) and Chin (CH), together
Exercise is healthy,	Collarbone (CB), both together
reading has great value!	Under the Arm (UA), both together
Every day I get better and better,	Cross wrists over one other
and so much...	Cross back of hands one over other
happier too!	One hand over other, both on Crown of Head (CRH)

11.3: EFT for cravings and addictions

> *"Prayer indeed is good, but while calling on the gods, a man should himself lend a hand."*
>
> **— Hippocrates**

I often carry chocolates and chips to my workshops for demonstrating EFT. Frequently, the large size image of attractive chocolates/chips in the powerpoint presentation triggers cravings in the audience. Mehek was one such participant, who immediately let out a loud, "Wow... I want that!", the moment the slide came up. I invited her to come up for a demonstration. She said that she found chips irresistible and could never refuse one. Mehek also admitted that it was her favourite comfort food and she would often go overboard on multiple packets of chips when in low spirits. I pulled out a popular brand of chips. She was literally salivating already and when I asked her to open the packet, she laughingly said, "There is no way that I will not eat those chips now!" Her desire SUD was ten. I asked her to start tapping with, "Even though I can't wait to taste these yummy chips, I love, forgive and accept myself." I asked her to keep tapping until she had completed three short-cut rounds. I asked her to evaluate her desire for the chips again. She was very surprised and said it was down to three and she may actually be able to do without them! I asked her to remove a chip from the packet and smell it. She immediately got excited again and said her SUD had gone up to seven now. I asked to repeat three rounds using, "Even though I again want this chip, maybe I can do without it." After these rounds she was quiet and said, "I can't believe it, but I truly don't want to eat it!" implying her SUD was zero. I asked her to taste it anyway. Mehek reluctantly took a bite and kept away the chip saying, "I don't like the taste, I don't want it at all!"

I checked with her after about four weeks and she said that her desire for chips had come back only once. She tapped a couple of rounds on that occasion and never ate them.

EFT has demonstrated success in reducing intense cravings and in helping those who wish to overcome their addictions. Cravings and addictions are often, if not always related to emotional drivers. Consequent to the craved substance becoming a habit, there may be chemical or physical factors of withdrawal involved.

Treating addictions is a complex process and may require some time and help from an expert. However, to help you get started, here are some tips. Note that the full basic recipe is the preferred method in this case, but you may try the short-cut method as well.

Address the craving directly: For example, if you find you have an intense, irresistible urge to consume a chocolate, use set-ups like:

- Even though I *must have this chocolate*, I deeply and completely, love, forgive and accept myself.

- Even though I *crave this chocolate*, I forgive myself.

- Even though I *can't stop obsessing with this chocolate*, I accept myself.

- Even though I am *drooling at the idea of tasting this chocolate*, I deeply and completely, love, forgive and accept myself.

Modify the set-up using 'still have…' for rounds subsequent to the first one. The first time you try this, you will be astonished to notice the drop in craving intensity. Many people report a change in taste or even dislike to substances they have craved before tapping! This step alone, if repeated on a consistent basis, can help you overcome your irrepressible desires.

Address the substance for sensitivity: See 'EFT for substance sensitivity'. Very frequently, you are allergic to the substance that you crave. Several explanations have been proposed for this connection. As far as the EFT treatment is concerned, follow the suggestions given in the said section.

Address the habit: Include routine tapping for eliminating the habit. Notice when you need your 'fix' or what makes you want your drink, smoke, etc. Frame set-ups accordingly and tap these on a routine basis, as often as possible. Addictions can often be stubborn, hence the more frequently you tap the better.

Sample set-ups:

- Even though I *binge drink on weekends*, I deeply and completely love, forgive and accept myself.

- Even though I *must smoke after a meal*, I completely accept myself.

- Even though I *crave chocolates when I am lonely*, I deeply and completely love and accept myself.

You may also frame set-ups which are more suitable for the choices trio, such as:

- Even though I *need a smoke to cope with the stress*, I intend to be calm at all times.

- Even though I *can't do without my sweets*, I intend to adopt a low calorie diet now.

- Even though I *can't stop at one chip*, I choose to eat sensible portions now.

Address the blocks to giving up the addiction: This area would require a lot of introspection and detective work.

Try to figure out which beliefs limit your ability to give up this addiction. They may range from your own ideas or reflect opinions of others who are influential in your life. Sample set-ups:

- There is *no way I can give up this habit now,* but I intend to try.

- *Nicotine is a chemical dependency for me,* but I choose to kick the habit anyway.

- Even though *smoking makes me look cool,* I choose to be a non-smoking dude.

- *All the guys in my family are alcoholics,* but I choose to be a teetotaller.

Address the emotional drivers behind the addiction: Addictions are used as means to cope with emotional issues that may be too overpowering or distasteful to you. These will be the issues that you prefer to avoid or forget about. The craved substance may provide welcome *numbness,* or at least prove to be a significant distraction. The issue may be a current one, such as stress at work, or a troubled marriage or child. But it can frequently go back a long way, sometimes even involving childhood issues or traumas. Pay attention to when you got *hooked* and how you feel after you get your *fix.* Ask yourself questions like:

- Was there any significant change in my life at that time? A death, a job move or a house move, etc.

- Does the substance remind me of something? For instance, does smoking remind me of the comfort of feeling safe in my father's study, as a child?

- How does the substance make me feel? For example, sugar makes me feel less depressed, temporarily.

Once you have an idea to what your emotional drivers are (there may be more than one), you need to tap separately for all those issues.

Working with a *tapping buddy* or a professional EFT practitioner would be a good investment for those who are serious about quitting their habit.

Note: There have been many reports of proxy tapping helping significantly in the case of addictions. So if a near and dear one is overwhelmed by his addiction, you may consider starting proxy tapping. After some time, you may be able to persuade them to start tapping themselves as well.

11.4: EFT for abundance

> *"I keep the telephone of my mind open to peace, harmony, health, love and abundance. Then whenever doubt, anxiety, or fear try to call me, they keep getting a busy signal and soon they'll forget my number."*
>
> **— Edith Armstrong**

Yogesh was a salesman with a distributor company. He was appointed on a salary-cum-incentive basis, but was experiencing low confidence and poor results. Despondent and pessimistic, he would turn up unhappily for work and plod through his day, expecting things to be difficult. Yogesh's cynical expectation would be fulfilled and he would return home after selling few prducts.

EFT was first used to address his unenthusiastic approach to work using, "Even though I expect my day to be unproductive, I intend to put in my best efforts," and, "Even though I hate my job, I know I can be good at my work." After a few rounds of such tapping, he confessed that he didn't really hate his job, but that he was worried that he would not make enough sales to earn a good incentive. So he was then asked to tap, " Even though I am afraid I won't earn enough incentives, I intend to do my best everyday," followed by, "My enthusiasm and talent helps me achieve my targets easily." He said he felt far better and was keen to go to work the next day.

Daily morning rounds of, "I enjoy meeting with customers," and, "I effortlessly achieve my targets and earn significant incentives," were suggested. The very next day, he reported a change in his attitude and sales. He kept tapping and within days was pleasantly surprised by the significant improvement in his own performance. Within a few weeks, he was comfortably earning a satisfactory income and was going to work with eagerness and anticipation.

Another area where EFT can be used is, as a part of the strategy to improve abundance in your life. Abundance means 'profusion, plenty or large quantity'. Usually it is understood as *wealth*. However, when you are trying to apply EFT, or any manifestation technique, it would be advisable to identify with the larger meaning of abundance, namely a profusion of all kinds of blessings in your life, such as good health, relationships, love, joy, peace and material wealth.

Here is how EFT can help you LIVE an abundant life:

L   Letting go of limiting beliefs or blocks.
I   Implement improvements.
V   Visualisation and manifestation exercises.
E   Enhance existing strengths.

Letting go of limiting beliefs or blocks: This should first be identified carefully. Introspect and try to list all the negative beliefs or limitations that hold you back. It may be your own belief that you can never score 100 per cent in maths, learn swimming or get your complete bonus with a glowing appraisal. Such limitations often include the message we may have got from any authority figures in our lives, including our parents or teachers, for instance, if you were told 'you will never be good at languages' or broader clichés one often hears, e.g. 'females make bad drivers'. Even common beliefs such as, 'you should be taking care of others, thinking of yourself means you are selfish', 'listen to your elders, (even if they are wrong)', 'wanting material wealth means you are bad or materialistic', 'life is difficult', 'just like your father and grandfather, you will always be____' may have left a conscious or subconscious impact.

Do not exclude beliefs such as, 'I am bound to develop heart disease, it is in the family'. Remember that our understanding of hereditary conditions are being re-examined by epigenetics. Scientists have found that environmental exposure to nutritional, chemical and physical factors can bring about differences in gene expression. Which means that whether your genes are 'switched on or off' can be influenced by the environment.

Think back to the relevant memories that stand out in your mind. If you are able to identify any of them, use EFT to dissolve them. Also include incidents which left your confidence or beliefs shaken and continue to haunt you. For instance, one client not paying you on time may have left you cynical and suspicious, leading you to expect the same from nearly every client you encounter. Or losing your wicket and causing a match loss may have shaken your confidence as a winning batsman.

Affirmations such as the following may be employed:

- Even though my *grade seven teacher said I would never be good with numbers*, I intend to be a whiz with numbers now.

- Even though I am *afraid that my debtor will never repay me*, I intend to receive all my collections on time now.

- Even though I am *always broke by the end of the month*, I plan to manage my money efficiently now.

- Even though *both my parents had cancer*, I intend to enjoy a long and healthy life.

Implement improvements: If you are facing difficulty in adopting a disciplined attitude or new, helpful habits try EFT. Sample affirmations:

- Even though I *feel lazy to go to the gym*, I choose to be enthusiastic about my exercise routine.

- Even though *I tend to drink less water*, I intend to drink adequate water now.

- Even though I *tend to look at the dark side of things*, I choose to focus on the silver linings now.

- Even though I *never write up my accounts*, I choose to maintain accurate and timely records now.

- I choose to do my *riyaz* daily.

- I intend to meditate (or practise EFT) first thing every morning.

- I choose to improve my computer skills.

- I intend to respond to my calls and mails in a timely manner.

- I choose to explore new markets for my product.

- I choose to proactively work on new business opportunities.

Visualisation and manifestation exercises: These can be combined with EFT. There are plenty of books and websites which give details about exercises on how to vividly imagine your specific goals and other ways to help manifest your objectives. The law of attraction (the law of attraction implies that your thoughts create your reality) and similar ideas suggest that whatever you focus your attention on is drawn into your life. Sequentially tap on your EFT points, while doing such exercises, or watching story boards or slide shows depicting your goals.

Enhance existing strengths: Please refer to the sections on 'Strengths' and 'Opportunities' in 'SCORE with EFT', as also 'Gratitude tapping', for details.

11.5: EFT for relationships

> *"I've learned that people will forget what you said, people will forget what you did, but people will never forget how you made them feel."*
>
> **— Maya Angelou**

Manasi, a working mother of two children, a thirteen-year-old boy, and a nine-year-old-girl, had a challenging time with her son. His lifestyle, environment and peers were all quite different from the upbringing she had received in her paternal home. Her well intentioned but nagging approach towards trying to provide him with 'appropriate *sanskar*' was not well received. This strained the relationship between mother and son, with almost every conversation ending in a shouting match. This was followed by long bouts of sulky silence and the entire household was affected by anger, confusion and depression.

When Manasi heard of EFT, like many others, her first reflex was to try EFT to correct her son's behaviour. However, I suggested she first work on herself. As she began tapping on her anger towards him, she realised that her anger was more directed towards her husband, for *leaving the responsibility* solely on her. After tapping on this anger, her statements changed to, "I am not capable enough, so the responsibility overwhelms me." We kept tapping using the default set-ups for these phrases.

Manasi stopped at the end of about twenty minutes of tapping and revealed that what she actually felt was fear. She began crying and related that a cousin of hers had committed suicide as a young teenager. Prior to this day, Manasi had never realised that she was actually terrified that her son, with his teenage mood swings, depression and quiet spells was actually heading the same way. Her extreme controlling behaviour and underlying helplessness was largely driven by this fear, which had been subconscious so far.

EFT was used to collapse this behaviour, using set-ups like, "Even though I am terrified for my son, I love, forgive and accept myself," "Even though my son's moodiness makes me helpless, I choose to be balanced," "Even though I am afraid that my son will do the same thing, I know that they are two completely different people." I also told her to tap on, "I choose to radiate unconditional love, forgiveness and acceptance to my son and myself," as often as possible. Over a couple of weeks, EFT was used to address her many negative emotions and underlying fears, including her "guilt over spending too little time with the children" and "its all my fault, because I go to work." Manasi began to be much calmer and her communication with her son was more patient and reasonable.

Having noticed the change in her, her son, though still somewhat doubtful, agreed to try EFT for himself as well. He started tapping for his *anger towards mother, she doesn't understand me, it's all her fault, she doesn't care for me*, and then gradually moved over towards, "I know she is trying her best" and, "I intend to communicate peacefully with my family." We also addressed his self-esteem, self-consciousness and mood swings with good results.

Thanks to having understood and addressed their own issues, both mother and son now share a far more peaceful, understanding and caring rapport.

There are always two people involved in a relationship. But when things go wrong, the tendency is to focus on the mistakes made by the *other* person. Being focused on someone else's errors and shortcomings allows little scope for you to analyse and correct your own role in the situation. This is rather ironical, as clearly, we have more say and control over our own behaviour, attitude and responses, than over the next person.

Ideally, the two people could sit down and discuss matters in a loving, non-judgemental way. An honest and compassionate dialogue can improve matters significantly. Where differences are identified, EFT can be employed. Tapping on each other is a lovely way to connect and demonstrate the love and effort that each one is investing in the relationship.

Unfortunately, this is not always possible. Both persons may not be on the same page and such dialogue and techniques may not be welcomed by the other party. However, you can still get a lot done by using EFT yourself.

No matter as to whether this is a spouse, parent, child, sibling, friend, boss or co-worker. You are involved. So start working on yourself.

Note: In all cases, if you are unable to estimate a SUD, then tap five rounds.

Identify what attributes/behaviour in the other person triggers you and what is your emotional response: Do you feel unappreciated? Does that make you feel angry? Or helpless? Do you feel that X doesn't pay attention to your needs? Does that make you feel used, helpless or dominated?

Frame set-ups along the lines of:

- Even though X (*is doing/being___*), I deeply and completely love, forgive and accept X.

Bring the SUD for this set-up down to zero and follow this with tapping for a related set-up, along the lines of:

- Even though this makes me feel _____, I deeply and completely love, forgive and accept *myself.*

Tap on this set-up until SUD is down to zero.

Note: If you have difficulty in using 'love, forgive and accept him', then first do three to five rounds on your stumbling block, until you feel more comfortable using such a set-up — if you have trouble saying 'accept him', then tap using: "Even though I can't accept X, I deeply and completely love, forgive and accept myself."

Alternate set-ups for this issue: "Even though I can't

accept X, I would rather deeply and completely love, forgive and accept him." "Even though I can't accept X, I would rather be at peace."

After this, you can move on to set-ups like those listed below:

- Even though *X never appreciates my cooking*, I deeply and completely love, forgive and accept him.

  Even though *this makes me miserable*, I deeply and completely love, forgive and accept myself.

- Even though *X doesn't listen to my complaints*, I deeply and completely love, forgive and accept him.

  Even though *this makes me feel unimportant*, I deeply and completely love, forgive and accept myself.

- Even though *X won't even welcome me home with a smile*, I deeply and completely love, forgive and accept him.

  Even though *this disgusts me*, I deeply and completely love, forgive and accept myself.

- Even though *X expects me to run all the errands*, I deeply and completely love, forgive and accept him.

  Even though *this makes me feel used*, I deeply and completely love, forgive and accept myself.

- Even though *X doesn't compliment my looks anymore*, I deeply and completely love, forgive and accept him.

  Even though *this makes me feel old and ugly*, I deeply and completely love, forgive and accept myself.

- Even though *X takes credit for my work*, I deeply and completely love, forgive and accept him.

  Even though *this makes me furious*, I deeply and completely love, forgive and accept myself.

- Even though *X criticises all my efforts*, I deeply and completely love, forgive and accept him.

    Even though *this makes me miserable*, I deeply and completely love, forgive and accept myself.

Does the other person remind you of anyone?: This is a common occurrence and may go unnoticed, until you closely examine the pattern of behaviour between the two of you. Such associations with past negative experiences act as a significant contributor to the discord and can needlessly aggravate the new relationship.

Does the other person remind you of the way your father treated you? Or perhaps the way you perceived criticism from your mother? Maybe the other person makes you feel neglected by competing for attention and praise that you received before he came around, just the way you felt when your younger sibling was born.

Our brain is geared to look for patterns. Unknowingly, if you have associated the person or relationship with an older experience, you may be responding in the same way that you did to that person or situation. More often than not, this is likely to be inappropriate. If you suspect any such association, then tap along the following lines:

- Even though *X reminds me of* _____ ...

- Even though *X's temper scares me just as my father's did...*

- Even though *X makes me feel as insecure as my younger brother did...*

- Even though I *associate X's behaviour with (person/ event)...*

- Even though *I am reacting to X in the same way as I did to* _____ ...

Identify which of your attributes/behaviour trigger the other person: Be observant and notice any ways in which you may be provoking adverse responses. For example, do you nag over small things? Do you make unreasonable demands? Are you habitually late? Do you take the next person for granted? Are you told that 'you never remember' or 'you never listen'? Are you sloppy and untidy?

Frame set-ups along the lines of:

- Even though my (*doing/being___*) *upsets X*, I deeply and completely love, forgive and accept myself.

Bring the SUD for this set-up down to zero. Now be honest and examine whether there is any scope for you to improve or change with regard to this issue. Frame relevant set-ups like:

- Even though I _____, I now intend to _____

The choices trio would be an appropriate method for these set-ups.

Sample set-ups:

- Even though *my never being ready on time upsets X*, I deeply and completely love, forgive and accept myself.

    Even though I am *never ready on time*, I now intend to be punctual.

- Even though *my constant nagging irritates X*, I deeply and completely love, forgive and accept myself.

    Even though I *tend to nag X all the time*, I now intend to have more constructive dialogue with him.

- Even though *my frequent sulks anger X*, I deeply and completely love, forgive and accept myself.

Even though I *tend to sulk frequently*, I now intend to be more cheerful and upbeat.

- Even though *my careless work annoys X*, I deeply and completely love, forgive and accept myself.

  Even though I *am careless with work*, I now intend to work more sincerely.

- Even though *my gossiping hurts X*, I deeply and completely love, forgive and accept myself.

  Even though I *enjoy gossiping*, I now intend to use my time productively.

- Even though *my irresponsibility troubles X,* I deeply and completely love, forgive and accept myself.

  Even though I *am irresponsible*, I now intend to live up to my responsibilities.

Tap for improving the relationship: Frame an affirmative set-up that reflects how you would like the relationship to be. One of the most simple and effective set-ups I have found in this regard is: "I choose to radiate unconditional love, forgiveness and acceptance to X and myself."

Other examples include:

- I intend to have peaceful relations with X.

- I intend to have a more amicable relationship with X.

- I intend to be more patient and loving towards X.

- I intend to interact appropriately with X.

- I choose to have constructive communication with X.

- X and I provide loving support to each other.

- X and I share a mutually respectful relationship.

Using any one of the above approaches should prove helpful. But using all four methods is a systematic and thorough way of addressing all the issues between two people.

11.6: EFT at the workplace

> *"The principle is competing against yourself. It's about self-improvement, about being better than you were the day before."*
> — **Steve Young**

Manish was a team leader in a software company. While he had complete confidence in his technical knowledge, he would get nervous about the monthly presentations to his superiors. After discussions, we uncovered that there were two primary reasons why he dreaded these meetings. The first was his fear of public speaking and the second was his lack of self-belief regarding preparation of polished presentations.

The idea of addressing six to seven seniors would make him *tongue-tied* and *break out in sweat*. I asked him to visualise that he was addressing his seniors, and to imagine his SUD for these two factors. We tapped for, "Even though I get tongue-tied during my presentations, I intend to speak impressively now," until his SUD reduced from seven to zero. He said his SUD for *breaking out in sweat* had also reduced from eight to five. So we tapped two rounds for, "Even though I still break out in sweat at the idea of presentations, I choose to be calm and composed now." His SUD was now zero.

I asked him how he could improve his presentation skills. He sheepishly replied that he was too embarrassed to ask a colleague for guidance. Also, because of his earlier dread for the meetings, he would put off the preparations right till the last minute and naturally this only increased the pressure. So we tapped three rounds using, "Even though I am embarrassed to ask for help, I now request assistance easily and gracefully," followed by three rounds using, "I intend to prepare my creative presentations comfortably in time for the meetings."

After his very next meeting, Manish reported his progress. He said that he had been able to approach a colleague for guidance, who had given him several tips and information about websites to update his presentation skills. Encouraged by this knowledge he had worked eagerly on his slides and was well prepared on the D-day. At the meeting itself, he felt himself getting tensed up, so he discretely tapped under the table and felt calmer within a few minutes. Manish's presentation went well and the improvement was greatly appreciated by his seniors.

EFT can be used imaginatively in the workplace. People are using it not only to enhance their own performance and productivity, but also for improving internal relationships, team building, customer relations and target achievements.

Whatever may be your problem, once you have identified it, the easy way to use EFT is to apply the default set-up. Tapping on the issue directly helps by collapsing the negative beliefs, emotions and mindsets. Naturally, a more positive, confident, efficient and friendly mindset is bound to provoke a change in what you are able to accomplish and how others behave with you.

Tapping also seems to bring about better opportunities and solutions which may not have been apparent earlier. Perhaps these further changes may be explained by what is commonly described as the law of attraction. As suggested earlier, it implies that thoughts are created by your reality. By unblocking yourself and switching to thinking about your positive intentions, rather than your fears, you actually start attracting positive changes into your life. While this concept may seem a little unusual at first, there is no harm in trying it out for your self. At the very least, you would have addressed your own limitations. If any additional side-benefits accrue, so much the better.

Note that the guidelines given in 'EFT for relationships' can be used to improve relations with your boss, colleagues, juniors and clients.

Common emotions experienced in the workplace include:

- Feeling unappreciated
- Anxiety
- Anger
- Resentment
- Frustration
- Jealousy
- Guilt (when you know you are not performing to the best of your abilities)
- Boredom with routine jobs
- Deadline pressures

All these emotions can be addressed with the default statement and then followed by a round of positive intent. Alternatively, combine the negative component of the default set-up with the positive affirmation, and use the choices trio method.

For example:

- Even though *my boss never appreciates my contributions*, I deeply and completely love, forgive and accept myself.

  My innovative contributions to the project are well received now.

  (Even though my boss never appreciates my contributions, my innovative contributions to the project are well received now. Choices trio set-up).

- Even though *X's inefficiency maddens me*, I deeply and completely love, forgive and accept myself.

  I appreciate X's attempts to be more efficient now.

- Even though *X getting that promotion instead of me disgusts me*, I deeply and completely love, forgive and accept myself.

  I intend to perform so impressively that my increments and promotions are now inevitable.

- Even though *my boss sets for me impossible deadlines*, I deeply and completely love, forgive and accept myself.

  I choose to meet my deadlines with efficient ease.

- Even though I *feel guilty about slacking off at work*, I deeply and completely love, forgive and accept myself.

  I choose to put in my most sincere efforts now.

- Even though *I am thoroughly bored with this routine drill*, I deeply and completely love, forgive and accept myself.

I intend to find creative ways to learn, grow and perform at my interesting job.

- Even though *I just want to quit this awful job*, I deeply and completely love, forgive and accept myself.

  I intend to be productively employed with exciting and satisfying (or rewarding) work.

You can also use EFT for setting up the intention of a positive day, a productive meeting, supportive staff, etc. Examples include:

- I intend to have an exciting and satisfying day at work.
- I intend to enjoy work with a cheerful smile today.
- I intend that this meeting will smoothly and easily proceed to a mutually agreeable settlement.
- I intend to receive timely payments from my debtors.
- I intend to pay my EMIs comfortably and well on time.
- I intend to surround myself by principled and productive staff.
- I intend to have a cohesive, skilled team that enjoys overcoming challenges.
- I choose to make a brilliant and convincing presentation today.
- I choose to have a productive brainstorming session with my team today.
- I choose to find a creative solution to this problem.
- I choose to apply my talents productively.
- I choose to use my work hours with complete efficiency.

- I choose to be calm and confident at all times.

- I choose to find innovative and efficient ways of meeting my goals.

- I choose to experience perfect health and well-being at all times.

- I choose to be a key contributor in our productive sales team.

- I choose to meet my targets comfortably.

- I choose to have warm and friendly relations with my customers.

- I intend to continuously improve my knowledge base and skill set.

As you can see, there are numerous and diverse ways in which you can frame your set-ups to tackle issues at your workplace.

Consider introducing EFT to your colleagues. Propose a joint tapping session of five minutes at the beginning and the end of the day. Such group sessions have shown significant improvements in team building, sales, etc. The collective tapping for common goals will lend a sense of purpose and bonding to each employee.

11.7: EFT for pain management

> *"Promise me you'll always remember: You're braver than you believe, and stronger than you seem, and smarter than you think."*
> — **A. A. Milne**

For almost four years, Amit had suffered from migraine attacks at least once a week. The pain would be intense and he would throw up, avoid light and lie groaning in pain for hours until the attack passed.

He approached me whilst having a severe migraine attack. He declared that the pain was excruciating (SUD nine) and sensitivity to light was ten. We started with, "Even though I have this excruciating migraine attack, I love, forgive and accept myself." The pain reduced only marginally. I asked him to drink more water and then tap using, "Even though experience tells me that this pain will last for hours, I would rather let it go!" After completing a full basic recipe round, he was astonished to notice that his SUD had reduced to eight. I was also surprised, though not for the same reasons. I was looking for a more significant reduction in the pain. I asked him to tap using, "Even though this reduced pain is good, I would rather have it go away completely." At the end of the round, his SUD was now four. He would have been happy to stop, but I suggested we try a few more rounds. We continued tapping with, "Though I can live with this much pain, I release all the remaining pain now." After two rounds his pain was zero. Amit was completely taken aback because he had never experienced such quick relief, not even after taking painkillers. I asked him to rate the light sensitivity. He said that it was down to two, even though we had not tapped directly for it. One round of, "I am comfortable with light now," reduced that to zero as well.

I told him to use the same set-ups if the migraine recurred. However, he was also to tap two daily rounds using, "Even though I tend to get migraine attacks, I love, forgive and accept myself." Amit reported that the gap between attacks kept increasing and he could bring down the pain with EFT every single time. After about two months, the attacks had stopped.

Considering the number of physical issues which have benefited by the use of EFT, it would take several books to cover this area in any detail. However, I have included a brief introduction to pain management, as even a minor headache can be a major deterrent in the full expression of our talents. As it stands, back and neck aches, frozen shoulders, migraines, arthritic knees, restless legs, etc. are all commonly prevalent in the general population.

Before you begin tapping for your pain, you may want to tap on any limiting beliefs using set-ups like:

- Even though I cannot believe that EFT can take away this intense pain, I choose to give it a fair try.

- Even though only painkillers/injections can relieve my pain, I choose to try EFT anyway.

For chronic pain, or pain due to serious disease, it is recommended that you first use the belly button correction method, explained in 'When You are Not Seeing Results'.

Different approaches to pain management include:

Tap directly on the symptoms: This is the most simple and direct approach. Identify the location as precisely as you can. Use a descriptor that is adequately representative for you. Tap for the symptom directly using set-ups like:

- Even though I have this *excruciating headache in my left temple*, I deeply and completely love, forgive and accept myself.

- Even though I have this *gripping pain in my right shoulder*, I choose to release it now.

- Even though *my knees are painfully locked*, I give myself permission to move freely now.

- Even though *my body aches all over*, I choose to experience perfect health and well-being now.

Tap with modified set-ups, until SUDs are down to zero.

Chasing the pain: Strangely enough, even pains that are due to mechanical causes such as injuries, can often show change in location and or quality, as we continue to tap. For example, what may originally be a neck pain, may move down to the shoulder, then down the arm, etc. The pain may change in intensity or nature. For example, a throbbing pain may change to a stabbing pain or a dull, nagging one. In all cases, keep addressing the fresh location and quality with suitably changed set-ups. Do not be alarmed by these *shifts*. In fact, they are indicative of healing happening at the core level. Eventually, sufficient rounds should bring you relief.

Use of metaphors: Many people, especially those who are more visual or kinaesthetic, seem to get faster relief by describing the pain with metaphors. You can frame set-ups in accordance with the metaphor you have chosen. For example, *rocks on my shoulders* may describe aching shoulders. You can then use: "Even though these rocks are weighing my shoulders, I choose to throw them off now."

Or if you use *fire in my stomach*, to describe burning cramps in your stomach, a relevant set-up would be: "Even though I have this fire burning in my stomach, I choose to extinguish it now." You can let your imagination loose and tap while saying, "Cool water is now putting out this fire in my belly", repeating this sentence at all points while visualising the whole scenario in your mind.

Bundling/Boxing technique: (A particular form of metaphor use). In the case of chronic pain, or pain caused due to various emotional and or physical factors, you may prefer not to go into the details of each contributor. In this case, you may require more rounds of tapping. But you can avoid listing each and every item that contributes towards the pain. Imagine a big box or trunk, and start tapping with the set-up: "I choose to place all the contributors to this pain into this box." Do a full round using this set-up and then pick a way that you would like to be rid of this box. You may want to hand it over to God/angels, if your beliefs support such ideas. Or you may simply wish to burn it away like garbage, or dissolve it into the sea. Whatever your chosen method, visualise the scenario and tap with an appropriate statement, like, "I choose to burn away this box and all the pain with it."

Repeat the whole procedure until pain is sufficiently reduced.

Substance sensitivities: Sensitivites are often contributors towards persistent pain. Candida or systematic yeast infections have been associated with chronic pain and fibromyalgia. If you suffer from this, as a precautionary measure, you could tap at least three rounds for each of the following set-ups:

- Even though I may have a problem with yeast…
- Even though I may have a systematic yeast infection…

Surgical implants and medicines can also be culprits. Please see 'EFT for substance sensitivities' for more information.

Identify any emotional contributor: Many of you will already be familiar with the concept of the mind-body connection. This view proposes that our emotions and thoughts strongly influence our physical health. Put differently, any emotional stress is likely to impact your body and may amplify any existing weakness. Hence, one option is to work on this emotional contributor. Questions like the following can help you identify a contributing emotion or event:

- When did this pain start?
- What was happening in your life at that time?
- When does it seem to worsen? Does any person or situation seem to aggravate it?
- When does the pain seem to be less?
- What does the pain prevent you from doing? Are you trying to avoid doing that?
- Is there anything which makes you feel guilty?
- Do you feel that you 'deserve' this pain?

Once you have identified any possible triggers, tap for those separately and as a side benefit, you may experience relief from the pain. Refer to 'General Guidelines for Framing Set-ups and Reminder Phrases' for help with framing the relevant set-ups.

11.8: Gratitude tapping

> "When you are grateful fear disappears
> and abundance appears."
> — **Anthony Robbins**

Vidya, a middle aged housewife, spent almost the entire time in her first session, complaining about every possible thing in her life. Her husband travelled for his work and was rarely at home. Her two grown up children had recently moved to another city for their studies. Vidya was lonely, depressed and resentful because she still had to be submissive to her autocratic mother-in-law. We identified specific events and beliefs to work on during our appointments.

However, I suggested that if she wanted to experience a significant shift in the way she perceived her life, she should start daily gratitude tapping, using, "I am grateful for_____ today."

At first, she resisted saying, "I can't think of anything. My life is in a mess. I end up doing all the work and everyone cribs..." So I told her, to begin with identifying events/things that made her day bearable if not happy. For example, the TV program she enjoyed, for a change, her mother-in-law not complaining about the morning meal, a chat with her friend, and so on. She reluctantly began tapping on not more than three items the first week. At the end of the week, she sounded a little brighter and said it was becoming easier to find things to be grateful for. Gradually, over time, Vidya began to be enthusiastic about this exercise and noticed a shift in her own attitude.

After about a month, she reported that she was feeling calmer. Her habit of appreciating others and their role in her daily life was being noticed and they in turn were more appreciative of her fresh and happy attitude towards life. She was surprised to see how all her relationships had improved. She had rediscovered her love for painting and had joined art classes. More productively occupied, her entire attitude was radically different from the tired, complaining and victimised approach that she had earlier.

Bogged down by our daily problems and taxing routines, we frequently forget to appreciate the good things in our life. Our trials and tribulations tend to take up all our attention and energy, while the better parts are taken for granted or are neglected.

No matter how difficult your situation may be, if you look for them, you *will* find many people and things to appreciate in your life. If you look only for stress and sadness that surrounds you, it is all you will notice. *Seek and you shall find.* Once you have made up your mind to appreciate things, you will begin to notice a long list of blessings.

Start with the basics. You are literate and have enough money, understanding and time to seek improvement techniques as are provided in this book. In all probability, you have all the basic amenities required to live with dignity.

Now notice the small and unpretentious little additional benefits. Notice the sunny smile on a child's face, or the chirping bird outside your window. Be grateful for the maid having turned up on time. Or because you were on time for your 8.00 am train. Be thankful that you updated your virus database yesterday, just in time to catch the virus that was accidentally downloaded today!

Move on to more significant matters. Appreciate a family member or friend who has stood beside you through thick and thin. Become aware of the beauty in people, Nature, animals and objects, that moves you in a genuine and profound way. Be grateful for any of your own personal attributes that you admire, like your caring nature, mental strength or determination.

You can make this attitude a part of your very personality, by tapping on things you feel grateful for. This attitudinal shift will bring about a sense of hope and lightness that may have been lacking earlier. Whenever you are feeling low, switch your thoughts to anything that makes you feel grateful and tap using set-ups like: "Even though I am feeling low, I am grateful for____."

Ideally, make gratitude tapping a part of your routine. Every night, make a list of at least three things that you are grateful for and tap a round of, "I am grateful for___' or, "I appreciate___," for each of these three items.

Try out this simple suggestion for yourself. You will be amazed at the results.

12 | Innovative Ways to Use EFT

*"Just as energy is the basis of life itself,
and ideas the source of innovation, so is
innovation the vital spark of all human
change, improvement and progress."*
— **Ted Levitt**

The earlier chapters explain various ways to use EFT for the common challenges that each of us faces on a daily basis.

But EFT does not have to necessarily be used for specific issues or in any routine, fixed way. Flexible and adaptable, EFT can be woven into other areas or practises that already exist in your life. Like water, it blends easily into every technique, and enhances the effect, without adversely interfering in the original system.

Use your imagination to come up with inventive ways to use EFT. In all cases, just keep tapping through the tapping sequence, starting from the KC point. Don't worry about which point you are tapping, just run through the entire tapping sequence, Here are some illustrations to get you started:

Tap on your favourite songs or poems: Most of us are fond of songs and music. Select songs with uplifting or inspirational lyrics and sing or play them, as you tap. You are free to choose a song from any language and if you have difficulty in selecting one, just search the Internet for *motivating lyrics.* The accompanying music usually makes the whole EFT process even more enjoyable and uplifting.

You could even make up your own song or poem and make an audio/video recording for yourself, personalise this idea to incorporate your own specific affirmations. For example, the makeover routine in SCORE may be worded like a song or rhyming poem. Recording it in your own voice, makes it very convenient to use, as you do not need to memorise all these lines and can pay more attention to the tapping, than on getting anxious over recalling the words.

Tap on your favourite prayers or mantras: If you are in the habit of praying or chanting mantras, then tap alongside. You will notice a profound shift in energy almost immediately. Prayers like the St Francis prayer are ideally worded. *Thy will be done, Om Shanti Shanti Shanti, Gayatri Mantra, Mahalaxmi Kavacham, Maha Mrityunjaya, Mool Mantra, Om Mani Padme Hum, Lotus Sutra, Green Tara Mantra,* and many others, all invoke a great sense of peace and well-being. If you select a long mantra, prayer or *shloka,* you can change tapping points mid-sentence or mid-way. Do not worry about getting it *right.* There is actually no way to go wrong!

Mirror tapping: Stand in front of a mirror and look directly into your own eyes as you say the set-up and reminder phrase and tap along. Many people find this to be particularly impressive.

Visualisation and EFT: For those of you who are familiar with visualisation techniques, you can use EFT alongside your visualisation exercises. For example, visualise your *dream home* in great detail and silently tap on all the EFT points. You can even tap while watching a slide show or storyboard that depicts whatever you are working on.

Tap on another person or buddy tapping: You can try tapping for a parent, spouse, child, friend, etc. You can request them to tap on you. The touch and compassion of another person can enhance the effect.

Discrete tapping: In a public situation, you may not feel comfortable running through the entire EFT procedure. In such cases, discrete tapping can be invaluable in reducing the intensity of your emotions, without making it too obvious to others. Tapping the KC point lightly, striking it gently like a karate chop, or even soft thumps of a closed fist are all of immense value. This alone can bring SUD down, when you are tapping during the event. Pressing the points around the eyes can look like you are trying to get rid of a headache. You can tap on your finger points, as it is easy to tap the hand points behind your back or under the table. Another way to stimulate the hand points is to keep a point pressed, as though you were clasping your hands together. However, one of the most discrete ways to get tapping is to tap the finger points of the left hand, with the left hand itself. The ring finger is also touched in this method, as the same meridian continues to the gamut point. The same applies to the right hand. The photographs illustrate how you can do this.

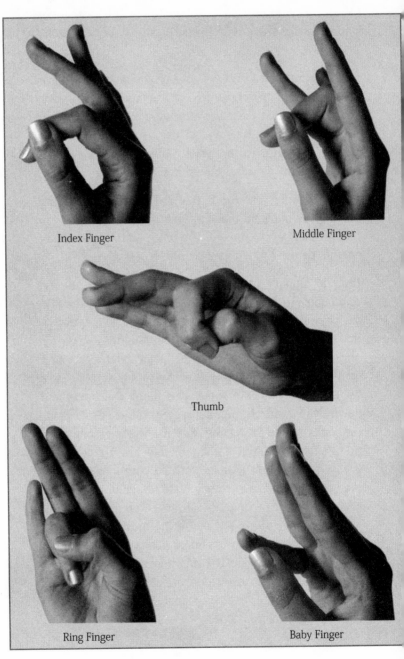

Index Finger

Middle Finger

Thumb

Ring Finger

Baby Finger

Discrete tapping

Imaginary tapping: If you are comfortable with visualisation, you can try imaginary tapping — without actually doing any physical tapping, imagine yourself going through the tapping sequence, while mentally reciting the set-up and reminder phrase. Many people have reported success with such tapping. However, those who generally have difficulty with visualisation exercises may not see the same level of success with this method.

Enhance meditation: If you have difficulty in being regular with your meditation and other practises, a daily round of, "I choose to consistently and consciously work at my self-improvement/spiritual growth," will help.

You can address any distractions or disturbing thoughts with EFT, to *clear* your mind before commencing meditation. A set-up that can deepen your meditative state significantly: "I choose to reconnect with my higher self." Use this before your meditation. At the end of your session, you may like to finish with a round on, "I choose to radiate unconditional love and acceptance to myself and all around me."

13 | In Closing

As you have seen, EFT is versatile and can be used in all areas of your life. Avoid the temptation to use EFT only as a 'first-aid measure', to obtain relief from an acute problem.

Instead, I urge you to incorporate EFT into your daily routine. Using a systematic approach, as the one outlined in SCORE, you can continually transform yourself into a better person. Just as you need food, exercise and sleep everyday, to take care of your physical body, EFT can be the tool that provides care and repair for your mind, body and soul. Don't forget that there is *always* room for improvement. Unless you happen to have a visible halo, you can safely conclude that there are areas and aspects which require your attention!

We all tend to get lost in the mundane demands of everyday life. But the larger questions remain in the background, waiting for you to seek them out. When faced with a life threatening situation, people suddenly have rapid shifts in their attitude. Regrets, hopes and aspirations are all suddenly cast with different priorities.

Richard Bach wrote: "I gave my life to become the person I am right now. Was it worth it?"

It's a question worth pondering.

Why wait until you are short on time? Your spiritual quest may redefine how you use the rest of your days. Regular use of techniques like EFT has an almost meditative effect. In the long run, you will find that not only are you able to resolve the pressing emotional and physical issues that currently drain your resources, but that you are more inclined and able to seek a more meaningful way of being.

Last but not the least, do share this simple technique with anyone you can reach out to. Many of us are unable to afford the expensive mental, physical or spiritual health care that we may so desperately need. Widespread knowledge and use of this inexpensive, relatively safe and effective technique can transform the very fabric of our society.

We are all, in a way, responsible for the present state of affairs in our world, either by our action, inaction or insufficient action. You now have a powerful tool that can help you actualise your own highest. However, you can also resolve to use EFT to inspire healing, development and growth in many others.

14 | Useful Websites

Author's EFT website:
http://www.soulspeakindia.com

Gary Craig's official EFT website
http://www.emofree.com

Attracting Abundance with Dr Carol Look
http://www.attractingabundance.com

Dr Patricia Carrington's website
http://www.masteringeft.com

Success Beyond Belief with Brad Yates
http://www.bradyates.net

EFT videos by Brad Yates on You Tube:
http://www.youtube.com/user/eftwizard

Dr Barbara L. Mallory's website
http://feelingfree.net

EFT Forums
http://emofree.com/forum_landing.htm

EFT for Juniors
www.soulspeakindia.com

TATLife, Tapas Acupressure Technique
http://tatlife.com/

Nithya Shanti's websites
http://www.lovingsilence.org
http://groups.to/happiness
http://in.youtube.com/user/nithyashanti

EFT – Vision India
http://groups.to/eftindia